Ceramics in the Modern World

Aldus Science and Technology Series

Ceramics in the Modern World

Man's First Technology Comes of Age

Maurice Chandler

 Aldus Books London

First published in the United Kingdom by
Aldus Books Limited, Aldus House, Fitzroy Square, London, W.1
Printed in Italy by Arnoldo Mondadori, Verona
Distributed in the United Kingdom and the Commonwealth by
W. H. Allen & Company, 43, Essex Street, London, W.C.2
Copyright © Aldus Books Limited, London, 1967

Contents

Suggested Reading

P. P. Budnikov, *The Technology of Ceramics and Refractories*, Massachusetts Institute of Technology (1966).

F. H. Clews, *Heavy Clay Technology*, British Ceramic Research Association (London, 1955).

A. E. Dodd, *Dictionary of Ceramics*, George Newnes (London, 1964).

R. W. Ford, *Drying*, British Institute of Ceramics Textbook Series, MacLaren (London, 1964).

W. F. Ford *The Effect of Heat on Ceramics*, British Institute of Ceramics Textbook Series, MacLaren (London, 1967).

F. J. Goodson, *Clay Preparation and Shaping*, Brick Development Association (London, 1962).

A. T. Green and G. H. Stewart, *Ceramics*, The British Ceramic Society (London, 1953).

J. E. Hove and W. C. Wiley, *Modern Ceramics*, John Wiley (New York, 1966).

W. D. Kingery, *Ceramic Fabrication Processes*, John Wiley, (New York, 1958).

F. Moore, *Rheology of Ceramic Systems*, British Institute of Ceramics Textbook Series, MacLaren (London, 1965).

Alan W. Norris, *Properties of Fired Materials*, British Institute of Ceramics Textbook Series, MacLaren (London, 1967).

F. H. Norton, *Ceramics for the Artist Potter*, Addison-Wesley (New York, 1956).

F. H. Norton, *Elements of Ceramics*, Addison-Wesley (New York, 1952).

P. Renault, *Pour le Ceramiste*, 2 Volumes, Dunod (Paris, 1954).

A. B. Searle and R. W. Grimshaw *Chemistry and Physics of Clays*, Benn Brothers (London, 1959).

W. E. Worrall, *Raw Materials*, British Institute of Ceramics Textbook Series, MacLaren (London, 1964).

Preface

Ceramic products touch upon our lives at widely differing points. Ming vases and lavatory basins, synthetic diamonds and bricks, high-voltage insulators and dental fillings, flowerpots and radioactive waste absorbers, drainpipes and memory cells, spark plugs and blast-furnace linings—their very variety makes a definition difficult. For if we ask what distinguishes these from nonceramic articles the answer will be a definition containing a number of important elements, to each of which, however, some exceptions must be allowed. They are *almost* all shaped at room temperature and then permanently hardened by heat; *most*, not all, are made wholly or mainly of clay or some other natural earth

Ceramists began working at their trade before the great pyramids were built, and the exceptions made in defining their products have become necessary only in the past 70 years or so. For some 70 centuries before that, therefore, all ceramic articles could be simply defined as articles shaped out of clay and permanently hardened by heat. The definition may be simple but the ceramist's craft was not. Clay, his raw material, differed widely in physical properties and chemical composition not only from one natural deposit to another, but also within the same deposit. Shaping called for processes ranging from hand modeling with all the skill and artistry of a sculptor, to casting in intricate molds; from throwing on the potter's wheel to turning on a lathe; from powder-pressing to mechanized extrusion and slicing. The wet clay that lent itself so well to all these shaping methods was not easy to handle without causing further and unwanted changes of shape. Besides, if it went straight to the kiln, the water in it would turn to steam with disastrous consequences to the wares. So the shaped articles first had to be thoroughly dried, in the interior as well as on the surface, to prevent the setting up of stresses and strains that might result in cracking during firing. Glazes had to be prepared in such a way that their rate of expansion when heated bore a certain relationship to that of the clay "body" to which they were applied, otherwise they would tend to either crack or peel. Decoration demanded a knowledge of coloring oxides and inorganic pigments that would give the desired colors after they had been subjected to high temperatures that often changed their chemical composition.

Finally the ceramist had to contend with the hazards of firing. Until the turn of the present century only solid fuels were available, and open-flame kilns (as opposed to *muffle* kilns, which are heated from the outside of the refractory chamber) were infernos of smoke and naked flame; yet the ceramist had to see to it that his delicate wares emerged unmarked. Imperfect dampers and draft systems, ignorance of the precise calorific value of the fuel, and the necessity for periodic stoking made it impossible to exercise strict control over kiln temperatures; and, to add to the difficulty, there was no reliable method of measuring high temperatures until well into the 18th century. But if the ceramist did not raise the temperature to the necessary level for the necessary length of time, his wares would not vitrify sufficiently to make them rock-hard; if he raised the temperature too high, for even a short time, they might melt into a shapeless mass.

In short, ceramists wrestled with complex physical problems long before there was a discipline called physics, and came to grips with high-temperature chemical reactions centuries before the advent of chemistry, or even alchemy. It was not until this century that scientific research had any marked effect on ceramic materials and processes.

Since then the scope of the ceramist's work and the range of his raw materials have widened rapidly. He now employs shaping methods such as dry-pressing and injection molding, which are not traditional to his craft; he develops and works with material such as silicon carbide, uranium dioxide, and silicon nitride, which have little in common with naturally occurring earths; and it happens more frequently now that hardening by heat is not the last link in the chain of manufacturing processes. All this explains why the simple definition of ceramics already given, though applicable up to the end of the 19th century, must be modified in the 20th. Today, a ceramic material may perhaps be defined broadly as any nonmetallic inorganic substance in the solid state, usually a compound, frequently an oxide. But even this definition breaks down when we come to a material like carbon, which is considered as a ceramic because of its highly refractory nature rather than because of any intrinsic characteristic relating it to other ceramic materials. In fact it is now no longer possible to define ceramics in terms of composition at all. Instead they must be defined as materials that lend themselves to manufacture in a certain way, the essential part of which is the application of heat in one form or another, to render them hard and resistant to their environment.

The modern extensions of ceramics are of great importance to high-temperature engineering, rocketry, and electronics, but this should not blind us to the fact that the less glamorous traditional products of the ceramist are still of great importance to comfort and convenience in everyday life. If there were no bricks or dinner plates it would be a poor consolation to know that there were plenty of ceramic magnets and rocket nozzles. Thus even in so brief a book as this it would be a mistake to concentrate on the novel to the exclusion of the traditional. It would also be grossly misleading, for science and technology now play a great part in the manufacture of traditional ceramic products as well as in that of newer ones. And scientists are not yet within reach of completing their investigations into the properties of clay, the oldest and still by far the most widely used of all ceramic materials.

1 Clay and Bricks

Not only are bricks among man's oldest ceramic products; they are still, in the 20th century, among the most widely used of all building materials. The reasons for this are to be found in the very nature of clay itself—its widespread, seemingly unlimited, natural deposits, the comparative ease with which it can be shaped, its rigidity when dried, its strength when fired. Bricks, therefore, make an excellent beginning to a survey of man's oldest industry and its adaptation to the needs of today. In this chapter, after examining the nature of clay and the history of bricks, we shall take a close look at modern brickmaking processes, from clay-winning and shaping to the control of firing temperatures.

What is Clay?

In order to answer this question we must first take a quick look at crystalline rocks such as granite and gneiss, which form the greater part of the outer crust of the earth. These rocks are, in the

Opposite: China clay is a hydrated aluminum silicate extracted from decomposed granite. This 80-meter-deep china clay pit, one of the largest in Cornwall, England, produces six million kg. of refined china clay per week. After the removal of the topsoil or overburden, the pit face is power-hosed and the resulting clay-bearing slurry is pumped away. Waste sand is then removed and the clay stream passes to a series of large dewatering tanks from which the china clay is removed by a process of sedimentation. It is then refined and dried in mechanical drying plants, ready for shipment in bulk or for milling and bagging.

main, heterogeneous mixtures of feldspar, quartz, and mica, the most abundant component being feldspar. Feldspar is the name applied to a number of mineral aluminosilicates, the most common being that of potassium (K_2O. Al_2O_3. $6SiO_2$) and the next most common that of sodium (Na_2O. Al_2O_3. $6SiO_2$). In fact nature never provides either in pure form; they are invariably found mixed, with one or the other predominating.

Ever since their formation, granitic rocks have been subjected to physical and chemical changes brought about by the action of water (often slightly acidic), ice, wind, and other natural agencies. The most marked physical effect has been the gradual breaking down of primary rock—especially near the surface—into fine-grained secondary minerals; and these fine-grained minerals, having a far greater surface area per unit volume, have been far more vulnerable to chemical attack. In view of the complicated makeup of the substances concerned and the wide variations in climatic conditions through the ages, such chemical reactions did not proceed with the same amenability to precise description as if they were the results of chemical experiments carried out in the controlled conditions of a laboratory. But we can at least summarize one reaction that must have been common when water containing dissolved carbon dioxide came into prolonged contact with potash feldspar:

K_2O. Al_2O_3. $6SiO_2 + 2H_2O + CO_2$
(Potash feldspar)　　(Water containing carbon dioxide)$\rightarrow$
Al_2O_3. $2SiO_2$. $2H_2O + 4SiO_2 + K_2CO_3$
(Clay-substance)　　(Silica)　(Potassium carbonate)

The clay-substance found in the reaction shown above is the ingredient common to all clays, but it is never the only one. Even if we confine ourselves to the products of the above reaction, we can see that the clay-substance may be mixed with silica. (The potassium carbonate, being water-soluble, will probably be washed out.) In addition we must remember that the starting-point of our formula takes no account of the quartz—also a form of silica—and mica present in the fine-grained granite rock. These, too, will commonly be mixed with the clay-substance. There may also be a small proportion of the primary feldspar that took no part in the reaction. In addition there will be small quantities of other impurities that were present in the primary rock, such as iron oxides and titanium dioxide. Some inorganic impurities will impart various colors to the pristine whiteness of the clay-substance: Ferric oxide (Fe_2O_3) will make it reddish, while limonite (a term covering most hydrated iron oxides) will make it buff.

In addition to inorganic impurities, aeons of plant growth and animal life may have introduced a considerable proportion of organic matter into some clays, turning them grayish or almost black. In brickmaking the combustion of this organic matter in the clay during firing can sometimes result in fuel-saving. But the color of raw clay is no guide to the color it will be when fired. *Ball* clays, for example, are sedimentary, extremely plastic clays that are dark in the unfired state because of organic impurities, but that become white or cream-colored when fired.

When clays are found where they were originally formed (which they are not very frequently) they are known as *residual* or *primary* clays. Often they were formed deep underground, the necessary chemical changes having been brought about by superheated acidic water that was forced up under pressure through the mass of primary granite. Clay deposits of this kind are commonly characterized by their great thickness—sometimes of several hundred meters, as in the clay deposits of Cornwall, England—and by their high content of large-grained primary minerals, such as quartz, mica, and feldspar.

Far more common than residual clays are sedimentary or secondary clays that have been transported, perhaps more than once, from their site of origin by the action of seas, rivers, and glaciers. These vary greatly in composition according to mode of transportation and age. Clays that have been pushed along by glaciers have usually mixed with the pebbles and gravel that accompanied them to form boulders, and the clay-rich parts of such deposits are known as *boulder* clay. Where a slow, meandering river has worn away its banks and changed its course frequently, it may have deposited clay, mixed with varying quantities of fine sand and soil, on either side of it; but because such deposits are highly variable in composition, shallow, and not usually extensive, they seldom warrant commercial exploitation. Fast-flowing rivers, carrying along rock fragments of many different

A selection of typical clays as received from the clay pit. Top row, left to right: Australian plastic clay, fireclay, and Wadhurst clay. Bottom row: Etruria marl and red marl.

sizes may reach a point (usually near the mouth) where the slope of the river bed suddenly becomes less steep, sharply reducing their velocity and causing them to drop minute particles of sand and other rock debris simultaneously. Deposits of sandy clay laid down in this way are often especially useful for brickmaking.

Naturally graded clay beds are likely to be found where a river flowed into a lake, depositing the largest of its rock-debris particles near the point of entry and carrying progressively smaller particles nearer and nearer to the center of the lake. The deposits so laid down tend to consist of thick layers of sand and gravel at one end, grading down through intermediate layers of sand and clay, to thin layers of almost pure, fine-grained clay (or possibly clay and chalk) at the other end. Similar but more extensive deposits are found where ancient rivers entered seas that have since receded, owing to the uptilting of coastal lands. There the clay is nearly always mixed with varying proportions of chalk or lime, probably representing the remains of minute seashells. The salt present when the deposit was laid down on the shallow seabed has by now been washed out by thousands of years of weathering.

The first clays to be formed, some 1000 million years ago during the Upper Precambrian Period, are no longer recognizable, or even classifiable, as such. Under the enormous pressure of later rock formations that came to overlie them, they have hardened into slate. Among the oldest clays still classifiable as such are the *flint* clays, a type of fireclay often found as an impurity in coal. Formed during the Carboniferous Period, some 250 million years ago, the flint clays have also been subjected to great and prolonged pressure, and have become hard and rock-like. At the other end of the geological scale many of the softer clays, including the extremely plastic ball clays, had their origin during the Tertiary Period, between eight and forty million years ago, while boulder clays, as we have already seen, date back only to one of the glaciations that have occurred during the past million years.

The word *clay* is therefore among the more troublesome of the single-syllable words. It covers a huge range of natural substances differing greatly in appearance, texture, and chemical and physical properties: Some, such as commercial kaolins, contain up to 90 per cent clay-substance, others, such as certain brick clays, as little as 30 per cent. The justification for applying a single generic name to all of them is that they have certain important qualities in common. They are all plastic when wet; when merely dried they are all rigid, but will regain their plasticity when thoroughly rewetted; when fired they all become permanently nonplastic and mechanically stronger.

The Beginning of Bricks

As early as the Paleolithic Age, observant hunters must have noticed how wet mud or clay took the clear impress of footprints. From this it would be only a short step to making some kind of impression by intent, and from this it would be natural to go on to the more useful experiment of hand-shaping lumps of mud and leaving them to harden in the sun. The experiment was to yield rich dividends in the Neolithic Age, when hunter turned farmer and needed a house. Suitable stones for building were not always available, and with stone tools timber construction was not easy. There were, however, few areas without some sort of clay or mud that could be made into bricks and dried in the sun. Although homes built in this manner would stand up well enough to light rain, a deluge would destroy them. As recently as this century, sepoys in the British Army in India were given regular annual leave to rebuild their mud and straw houses, washed down each year by the monsoon. The sundried mud-brick hut

Economic restrictions

proved its worth, however, and still plays a useful part in housing the world's millions.

Unfired bricks were also employed in projects far more ambitious than the building of small dwellings. Some 6500 years ago the Palace of Kish, in ancient Sumer, was built of unfired bricks, though its builders knew of fired bricks and used them for paving. The solid core of the step pyramid of Sakkara, the first of Egypt's vast pyramids, was of unfired brick, though the whole building was faced with stone or marble; so were the interiors of the massive walls of Babylon, though they, too, were faced with fired bricks or tiles. The fact that the builders used unfired bricks on such a massive scale when fired bricks were already known can be explained on economic grounds. The cost of providing fuel to fire all the bricks used in these vast structures would have been prodigious; and so long as they were faced with materials that would protect them from prolonged heavy rain, unfired bricks were quite adequate for the job in hand.

The makers of such bricks relied on only two of the characteristic properties of clay: its plasticity when wet and its rigidity when dried. The full and detailed reasons for the plasticity of clay are still a subject for argument among academic ceramists. Here it is sufficient to know that clay is plastic—that is, able to take on and retain a change of shape without losing cohesion when subjected to mechanical stress—mainly because of the shape of the grains of its clay-substances. The grains are extremely small, with a diameter seldom exceeding 10 microns (0.01 mm.), and, in high-quality clays, commonly having a diameter of less than half a micron (0.0005 mm.). With the optical microscope it was hard to recognize the structure of the smaller grains, but with the advent of X-ray analysis and the electron microscope we now know that all the grains are crystalline, plate-like, and almost two-dimensional. In any given mass of wet clay most of these crystalline plates tend to be stacked somewhat like packs of playing cards, and each grain is surrounded by water. The water acts as a lubricant, allowing the grains to slide easily over one another in the direction of the crystal plane when any part of the mass is subjected to mechanical stress, and also as a bond between grains, holding them together. When this water is dried out, the lubri-

Left: The way in which the crystalline, plate-like grains that make up a mass of wet clay are stacked like playing cards is clearly shown in this electron photomicrograph (x 9000). Below: stages in the drying of unfired clay. The surface film and most of the internal water (in A) dries out, causing shrinkage, resulting in the "leather-hard" condition (B). Next, water trapped in the angles of grains dries out more slowly because this is internal rather than surface drying (C). Finally, all "water of formation" is dried out, leaving a rigid, brittle structure (D).

A   B   C   D

cation disappears. The clay now has rigidity but only low mechanical strength.

Its low strength and the readiness with which it reverts to its plastic state when thoroughly wetted are the two chief defects of brick that is merely dried. Firing eliminates both. When clay is merely dried, the clay-substance loses its water of formation, i.e., the water surrounding the individual grains. When it is heated to a temperature of 450° to 550°C it loses its water of hydration, i.e. the water that previously formed an integral part of each crystal. What was formerly $Al_2O_3. 2SiO_2. 2H_2O$ breaks down, probably, into amorphous silica and amorphous alumina (SiO_2 and Al_2O_3). At this stage the material has become permanently nonplastic, but is weak and friable. At higher temperatures mica, feldspar, and other impurities in the clay dissociate into finely divided and highly reactive oxides. Some of these later combine with each other to form new crystalline phases, including needle-like particles of crystalline mullite, and some react to form a glass that permeates the whole structure, bonding the new crystals together.

Opposite, top: These adobe buildings at a borax mine in Death Valley, California, were put up in about 1880. Only in an arid region such as this (average annual rainfall is about 0.3 cm.) could sun-dried bricks last so well.

Below: fired bricks in the remains of a bath and various buildings in the Indus valley city of Mohenjo-Daro, probably built in about 2500 B.C. The idea of firing bricks to improve mechanical strength seems to have been discovered independently in widely separated parts of the world.

Men living in widely separated parts of the world hit on the idea of firing bricks, probably quite independently of each other, in remote antiquity. We have already seen that fired bricks were in use for paving in Sumer some 65 centuries ago; to the north, fired bricks of high quality and remarkable uniformity were used in the seventh century B.C. to face the famous Ishtar Gate of Babylon, built on the orders of King Nebuchadnezzar II; 4000 years ago bricks not unlike many of those in use today were a commonplace of architecture in the Indus-valley cities of Harappa and Mohenjo-Daro, and a large brick-kiln of the period has been excavated no great distance away, in Ahmadabad. However, especially built kilns were not essential, even though the people of the Indus and the methodical brickmakers of late Roman times commonly employed them. Bricks were frequently fired in what are called *clamps*. The method was to place a few layers of baked bricks on level ground, leaving channels here and there between them to hold fuel. The dried (or "green") bricks were next piled up on this foundation, with spaces for more fuel between them, and the whole mound was covered with clay or fired bricks to prevent loss of heat. The fuel was then ignited and allowed to burn itself out. The process might take many days, and this would be followed by a further long waiting period before the mound cooled sufficiently to allow the removal of the newly fired bricks. The brickmaker of ancient times was just as conscious of the need to economize on fuel as is his modern counterpart. The Egyptians especially, living where there was always a shortage of wood, mixed liberal quantities of chopped straw with the mud or clay. For bricks that were to be dried only, the straw served as a binder; for those that were to be fired, it served as fuel. A certain amount of other fuel was doubtless needed to start the firing, but thereafter the straw embedded in the clay began to burn, gradually raising the temperature of the whole clamp—so far as we can judge from the finished products—to something approaching 600°C.

Bricks fired at this temperature left much to be desired in the way of durability and resistance to water penetration. To improve these qualities to any great extent, as we have seen, meant firing at temperatures not lower than 1000°C, and this demanded the use of especially built kilns. Such kilns were in use in parts of the Middle East more than 4000 years ago, but it was the Romans of the first and second centuries A.D. who brought them to a high degree of sophistication and exploited them on a large scale. A typical Roman kiln was a brick-and-tile structure consisting of two chambers, the lower one serving as a fire chamber, the upper one as an oven in which the bricks were baked. Wherever possible it was built into the side of a hill, facing the prevailing wind, thus providing good draft for the fire tunnel. Almost the whole of the fire chamber, as well as part of the oven, was embedded in the hillside, an arrangement that not only cut down heat losses but also strengthened the kiln so that it could better withstand stresses set up by great heat. Hot gases from the lower chamber passed into the oven through vents in the oven floor, the front of which was situated very near ground level on the hillside to facilitate loading and unloading.

The Romans carried the art of high-quality brickmaking to areas of the Empire where it was previously unknown, including France, Spain, England, and parts of Germany. With it they also carried the techniques of manufacturing other heavy clay products, including roofing tiles and drainpipes. But with the collapse of the Roman Empire these arts fell into disuse in western Europe for the next 600 years. Not until the end of the 11th century was brickmaking revived in northern Italy, not until the 12th and 13th centuries did it reach the Low Countries and England, and not until at least two centuries later was it at all widespread throughout Europe. Thereafter, two circumstances in particular contributed to the increased popularity of bricks for building—a steady growth in population, and a steady decline in the amount of timber available near towns, due to the clearing of forest lands for agriculture. It is worth remembering that the city destroyed by the Great Fire of London in 1666 was mainly of wood because it was already old. The new city that rose from its ashes was built largely of bricks. In the America of that time, although there was certainly no shortage of structural timber, brickmaking had already been established for more than 50 years.

Until the early years of last century all bricks were handmolded. Then, following on the heels of the Industrial Revolution, came a great explosion of population and an unprecedented increase in urbanization and factory building; the demand for bricks soared, and only mass-production methods could hope to keep pace with it. This is not to say that handmade bricks suddenly became museum pieces. They continued to be made in quantity well into the present century, and even now bricks of unusual size, complicated shape, or special composition are handmolded in small brickworks. But as we shall see, most of today's bricks are made by mechanical methods.

Clay-Winning and Shaping

The three main brickmaking processes in use today are: the *plastic wire-cut* or *stiff mud* process, the *stiff plastic* process, and the *semidry* or *dry-press* process. But whichever process is employed, the first operation, and sometimes the most costly, is to dig out the clay from the ground and get it to the works. The digging (or *winning*, as it is called) is usually done with mechanical excavators such as power shovels, draglines, or shale planers, the last of which slice the clay from bottom to top of the pit face. The clay is then taken to storage sheds adjoining the works, by rail, heavy lorries, or conveyor belts. The works, of course, are sited as near as possible to the pit to minimize transport costs, and provision is made, so far as space permits, to store enough raw clay to keep work going when bad weather holds up clay-winning. At least two other economic considerations are important. First, a large modern brickworks may have an output of from a hundred thousand to over a million bricks per day, and if it is to be profitable it needs to remain in operation for perhaps 20 years or more. It is therefore essential that the clay deposit to be worked should be big enough to keep it supplied that long. (At a rough estimate it would need a layer of suitable clay 3 m. deep, and 1,000,000 m² in extent to maintain an output of 100,000 bricks per day for 20 years.) The second economic consideration is that the clay and the brickworks should preferably be within easy reach of busy building areas, to keep down the cost of delivery to the consumer.

Raw clay, more especially surface clay, usually contains various kinds of unwanted matter such as stones, small rocks, and woody roots, as well as inconveniently large clods of hard clay. A good deal of preparation is therefore necessary before it is ready for further processing. This can be done in many different ways, and the following are no more than outlines of possible sequences. First *jaw-crushers* may be used to break big lumps of hard material into pieces of around 1.25 cm. or less in diameter; next the clay may be passed through crushing machines in which several rollers rotating at different speeds both crush and grind it; heavy duty grinders may then be used to effect a further reduction in the maximum size of particles. Alternatively the clay may go to *edge-runner* grinding and mixing mills. The ground materials may then

A typical brick-clay pit, with dragline excavators at work. A layer of clay 3 m. deep and 1,000,000 m² in extent is needed for an output of 100,000 bricks per day for 20 years.

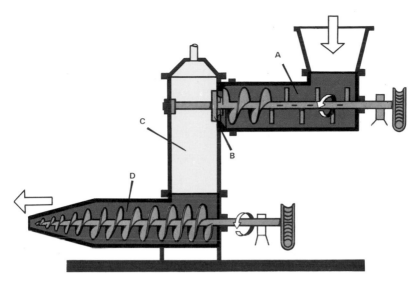

Cut-through diagram showing the action of a two-stage de-airing pug mill.
The clay is cut up in the first chamber (A), and forced through a shredding
plate (B) into a vacuum chamber (C). Here any air trapped in the clay during
cutting and shredding is removed. Next the shredded clay, now free from
air bubbles, is recompacted in the second chamber (D) and extruded as a
column of the correct consistency for slicing into bricks.

be passed through a series of sieves to eliminate all particles exceeding the maximum size desired, the rejected material being
returned for further grinding. In some cases up to 10 per cent of
particles as big as 0.25 cm. in diameter may be acceptable.

Except in the case of the semidry (or dry-press) process, the
clay, together with enough water to produce the required degree
of plasticity, usually goes next to a *trough-mixer*. This is an open,
cylindrical trough fitted with two parallel longitudinal bladed
shafts that rotate in opposite directions. From it the clay emerges
well mixed and with the right water content, but not yet compact.
To achieve compaction the mixture now passes to a *pug mill*. This
is essentially a large cylinder in which a series of knife-blades,
arranged in spiral formation, rotate on a longitudinal shaft,
pushing the clay forward and kneading it well. If the pug mill is
of the vertical type the clay, entering at the top, presses down,
under its own weight, toward the outlet near the bottom and in
these conditions the rotating knives cut through it and compact it
easily. In a horizontal pug mill the clay tends to turn with the
knives, and counter-knives are introduced to counteract this

26

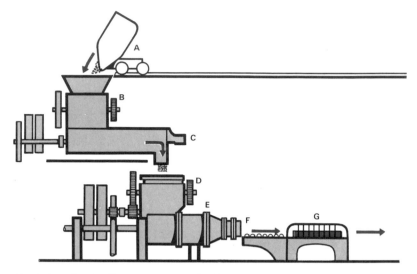

Typical production flow arrangement for the plastic wire-cut brickmaking process. Raw clay is tipped from a hopper (A) between the first set of rollers (B). It then falls into a feeder or trough-mixer (C), in which rotating blades mix the clay into a homogenous mass, supplying it evenly to a second set of rollers (D). From there it enters the pug mill (E), which compacts the clay. Next the clay is extruded through a die (F) that shapes it in the form of a column; this is cut in slices (larger than the size required, to allow for shrinkage during drying and firing) on the cutting table (G). The relative positions of feeder and rollers may be varied according to the nature and quality of the material used.

tendency. The kneading in the pug mill traps air bubbles in the clay, which could cause trouble during firing. Modern pug mills are therefore fitted with a vacuum chamber in which the pugged clay is shredded and the air removed. The shredded, de-aired clay then goes to the last part of the pug mill, where another rotating shaft drives it forward, the helical thread (or helically arranged knives) of the shaft being so arranged as to compress the clay in the process.

For the plastic wire-cut or stiff mud process the clay is next extruded from the pug mill (usually of the horizontal type) in a continuous column, through a die whose dimensions slightly exceed brick length and brick width. The taut wires of a machine rather like a large egg-slicer then cut the column into slices of slightly more than brick thickness. The raw bricks so made will shrink to the correct size during drying and firing. When fired, the two surfaces of the brick formed by wire cuts will be rough, while the four formed by the passage of clay through the die will be relatively smooth. The die dimensions and slicing arrangement described above mean that only the two largest surfaces of the brick—those normally in contact with mortar when a wall is built—will be rough. The *stretchers* (long, narrow surfaces) and the *headers* (short, narrow surfaces), which show in the wall, will be smooth and therefore not too liable to collect grime. The great majority of wire-cut bricks are side-cut in this way, but if end-cut bricks (stretchers and sides smooth, headers rough) are required for special purposes, die dimensions and wire-cutting machines can be modified to produce them.

The terms plastic wire-cut process and stiff-mud process applied to the extrusion method both indicate that the clay used must be of fairly high plasticity, and in fact it is often a rather soft surface clay with a water content of between 13 and 18 per cent. In the stiff-plastic process, widely employed in the northern English counties of Yorkshire, Lancashire, and Northumberland, the water content varies from 8 to 15 per cent, depending largely on the kind of clay, which is usually a hard laminated type (*shale*) or one with a high lime content (*marl*). The resultant mixture is a stiff paste that will flow only under high pressure. It is forced from a vertical pug mill into molds called *clot boxes*, set on a rotating table. The table then rotates part way, to a point where the paste in the molds is subjected to pressure exerted by mechanical presses. At the next part of the rotation the *clots*, or partially formed bricks, are forced out of the molds and removed from the table. They then usually go to another machine where they are pressed a second time to improve their finish.

For the semidry, or dry-press, process the clay must be in a state in which it can be ground or granulated by a dry-grinding process without inducing high plasticity; at the same time it must possess sufficient free water, so that when the ground clay is compressed in a mold box enough plastic deformation will take place to produce a coherent article. The water content can be anything from 5 to 20 per cent, depending on the kind of clay used. Although this process has been used in America for about a century, and although it is used in several parts of Europe to produce paving bricks, it is of special importance in Britain, where it provides a large proportion of all building bricks, particularly within a wide radius of London.

For many years a three-meter-thick layer of surface clay in the Peterborough area was used for making bricks of not very high quality by the plastic process. The story goes that at some time during the 19th century a workman cut down through the surface clay and struck far harder stuff. This harder, deeper clay came to be known as a *knot*. It proved to be part of the great belt of Jurassic clay, called Lower Oxford clay, that stretches from Yorkshire in the north to Dorset in the south. From it a colossal output of bricks is made by the semidry process. Such bricks are called Flettons, from the name of the village near Peterborough where they were first made. The clay from which they are made contains about five per cent by weight of carbonaceous matter,

The final stage of the plastic wire-cut brickmaking process, here making perforated bricks. Clay is extruded from the pug mill in a continuous column, wider and deeper than the bricks to be made. The taut wires of the wire-cutting machine slice the column into blocks slightly thicker than the required bricks. The clay will shrink to the correct size during drying and firing.

A selection of bricks made by the molding process. Although the bulk of bricks today are made by extrusion methods, difficult shapes such as those required for decorative copings, archways, and fireplaces are made by hand molding.

which considerably reduces the fuel requirements during firing.

Clay-winning for the making of Fletton bricks breaks down into two stages. First, a layer of Upper Oxford clay or *callow* up to seven meters thick must be removed, since it is too soft and plastic for the kind of brickmaking involved. Next the underlying Lower Oxford clay, commonly reaching a depth of between 15 and 20 m., is taken from the claypit or "knot-hole" by a mechanical excavator. At the brickworks it is crushed and ground in grinding pans, thereafter passing through perforations in the base of the pans to a conveyor belt, which takes it to a screen for grading. Coarse material is then returned for further grinding. The finer material, in the form of small damp granules, is elevated to the *hoppers* above the press machines. A moving carriage then discharges it into the open press molds where it is pressed between two pistons, one above, one below. The mass of granules, bonded under this pressure into a solid block, is then pushed out of the first mold into a second one directly in front of it, where it undergoes a second pressing.

In some parts of Europe the semidry process, first used only with hard, dry clays, is now also applied to soft, plastic clays, which must first be dried to render them suitable for pressing. This may seem a somewhat roundabout way of handling plastic clays that would lend themselves easily to extrusion and wire-cutting, but it produces bricks of exceptional strength and hardness, suitable for road paving. The pressure required to bond clay particles into a solid block increases with the dryness of the clay, and may be several hundred kilograms per square centimeter where the material is unusually dry.

So far we have looked at only the barest outlines of the various methods of shaping bricks by machinery, but it must be remembered that bricks are not always plain, solid, rectangular blocks. In fact, where extrusion is employed, dies can be shaped to produce hollow bricks (of increasing importance in modern building), or bricks with grooves on all but the wire-cut surfaces. Where molds are employed, their shapes (and the design of the piston ends that compress the clay) can be varied to give bricks with one or more curved surfaces (such as chimney or well bricks and "bullnose" bricks), or with some angles greater or less than right angles (such as "squints" and culvert bricks), as well as hollow bricks, and bricks with textured or deeply recessed surfaces. Special textures not dependent on the compression of the clay during its extrusion through a die or while in a mold can be obtained by combing, scraping, and imprinting, or by blasting sand, or particles of broken brick or slag, onto the green bricks. Roofing tiles, usually of similar clay to bricks, are commonly made by employing extrusion and wire-cutting to produce blanks and then pressing the blanks to the required shape.

Drying and Firing

After shaping comes drying—drying the interior of the product as well as the surface. Since bricks commonly have a small ratio of surface area to volume this thorough drying was formerly an extremely slow business. The oldest method, still occasionally used in small-scale seasonal brickmaking, was simply to leave a single layer of bricks to dry in the sun and air. This might take anything from a few weeks to a few months, according to the weather. Later, the drying process was speeded up by stacking the green bricks in lofts whose floors were heated either by steam pipes or by hot air rising from kilns underneath. Here the main drawback was the great number of man-hours required for loading and unloading.

Placing "green" (raw) bricks in the drying chamber. If placed straight in the hot atmosphere of the firing kiln, the surfaces would dry much faster than the interiors, and the difference in vapor pressure inside and at the surface would crack the bricks.

Today most bricks are dried either in especially constructed chambers fed with hot air or in long tunnel dryers, fitted throughout their length with temperature and humidity controls as well as fans to keep the air circulating. The tunnel dryer is usually heated by waste heat from the kiln—and indeed is sometimes an integral part of the kiln. The green bricks, stacked on cars, move slowly through it from one end to the other; when the drying is complete the cars go straight on into the kiln, thus eliminating manhandling between drying and firing. If the green bricks were plunged straight into a hot, dry atmosphere, the outside of them would dry first, and consequently contract; the interior, however, would be unable to shrink as it would not have lost its moisture, and the stresses set up would cause cracking. So in the first part of the tunnel the air is kept humid and not too hot, heating the bricks through gradually and evenly, but only slowly removing their water content. Further on in the tunnel the humidity can safely be decreased and the temperature raised, thus accelerating the drying. In the early stages of drying, as the water between the plate-like clay particles evaporates, the particles themselves come closer together, which accounts for the shrinkage that occurs. Eventually all the particles are in direct contact, a stage that ceramists describe as the leather-hard stage. But to say that all the particles are in contact does not, of course, mean that there are no spaces between them. There are such spaces, but when the water dries out of them there can be no further shrinkage until

Even small differences in firing temperature can have a marked effect on the color of the clay. The photograph shows clay (red marl), from left to right, as received from the claypit, and fired to 1150°C, 1200°C, and 1300°C.

firing; the dried-out spaces simply remain in the article as pores.

We saw earlier how the firing of clay to temperatures of 1000°c and above produces a glassy bond that gives the fired product permanent hardness and greater mechanical strength. During the firing process further shrinkage occurs as the pores previously existing in the dried brick are steadily eliminated. Shrinkage increases with increased temperature, but it is also influenced by other factors. The smaller the size of the particles, the greater will be the shrinkage. A high content of refractory materials, such as alumina, decreases shrinkage, while a high content of fluxes, such as mica and feldspar, increases it.

In ordinary building bricks some degree of porosity is desirable since it is this quality that gives them much of their value as heat insulators. The clay from which such bricks are made therefore need not consist of particles of very small grain size, need not contain a high proportion of fluxes, and need not be fired to particularly high temperatures, a peak in the region of 1000° to 1100°c usually being sufficient. Engineering bricks, used where great mechanical strength is the vital consideration and where

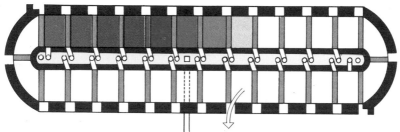

Above: plan of a side-fired continuous chamber kiln. It consists of 28 chambers separated from each other by coal-burning grates (gray) that are fired in succession around the kiln. Fuel is burned partly with cold air entering from outside, partly with hot air from chambers of fired bricks cooling down (shades of brown). At the same time hot air from the burning grate (orange) and the chamber actually being fired (red) is used to preheat bricks in chambers ahead (shades of pink). Chief advantage of this type of kiln is that fuel does not come into contact with the bricks. Fumes are conveyed by means of flues to a central chamber (yellow) from which another flue takes them to the chimney.

Below: bricks entering a 112-m.-long continuous tunnel kiln. Bricks, which take 72 hours to pass through it, are fired at the rate of 1700 per hour.

thermal insulation matters little (as, for instance, in lining railway tunnels and reinforcing embankments), must be as dense and nonporous as possible. The clays from which they are made often contain a higher proportion of such fluxing agents as iron and manganese compounds than clays used for common bricks, and they may be fired to temperatures up to 1300° or 1400°C.

Variations in body compositions and firing conditions affect not only the density of the finished bricks but also their color. Fired in an oxidizing atmosphere to a temperature of about 1050°C, various brick clays will yield red, yellow, brown, or near-white bricks, according to the impurities they contain and in what proportions, the most common color being red, due to the presence of ferric oxide. Yet from clays containing sufficient and identical proportions of ferric oxide it is possible to produce greenish, blue, or almost black bricks, as well as red ones. This is done by conducting part of the firing process in a reducing atmosphere (that is, one in which the burning fuel is denied sufficient atmospheric oxygen to combine with). In such an atmosphere the fuel robs the ferric oxide of some of its oxygen and the various reduced oxides so formed (possibly combined with silica) yield various colors.

Many kinds of kiln have been, and still are, used for firing bricks, but all can be placed in two broad categories, intermittent and continuous. The clamp and the Roman kiln described earlier were both of the intermittent type—that is, the green bricks had to be placed in them before firing could begin, and when firing was completed the bricks had to be removed. Over the centuries numerous improvements and variations have been effected in the design of intermittent kilns, some being equipped with up-draft systems, some with down-draft, most having only one firing chamber, but some having two or even more; and in the past few decades an increasing number have turned over to using gas or oil instead of coal, a change that makes for easier temperature control. But their greatest drawback—loss of heat resulting from periodic cooling of the kiln structure—has never been overcome, though some of the waste heat from the later stages of cooling can be utilized for drying or space-heating purposes. Even so, it is not uncommon for about one third of all the heat produced by the fuel burned at each firing to go into reheating the structure of the kiln. Partly to minimize loss of expensive heat, and partly to cut down the amount of labor involved in loading and unloading, most large brickworks now do their firing in continuous kilns.

The two kinds most widely used are called *ring-type continuous* or *Hoffman kilns*, and *continuous tunnel kilns*. The Hoffman kiln consists of anything from 12 to 80 adjoining firing chambers arranged in a closed circuit. Each chamber has its own external doors for loading and unloading bricks, and each is connected by its own flue, which can be opened or closed by a valve, to a single main flue. At any given time fuel is burned in only a few adjacent chambers, and this firing zone can be advanced, chamber by chamber, around the circuit. The firing zone therefore comes to the loaded bricks, not the bricks to the firing zone. Waste heat from chambers where firing has recently ended and that are now cooling is used to preheat air for combustion with the fuel in the current firing zone; waste heat from flue gases in the current firing zone is utilized to preheat the newly loaded dried bricks.

We saw earlier that Fletton bricks, shaped by the semidry process, are made from Lower Oxford clay, which has an exceptionally high content of carbonaceous material. Their firing, in Hoffman kilns, is therefore somewhat unusual. When still fresh from the press, with almost 20 per cent water content, they are loaded into a warm kiln chamber. After about 24 hours a controlled flow of hot air from the cooling zone of the kiln is introduced into the chamber, and this process continues for four or five days, until the bricks are thoroughly dry and warm. By this time the adjoining chamber is almost at full fire, and the dry bricks are subjected to the hot gases from it until the carbonaceous matter in the clay begins to burn. The heat so produced is sufficient to bring the bricks to the required firing temperature of 1050°c without the use of additional fuel. Indeed, there is some risk of over-firing, and to avoid this caps are removed from holes in the roof of the chamber, so that hot air can escape. After some eight hours the fuel content of the bricks is exhausted and the temperature starts to fall. The holes are then closed, and the bricks are allowed to stand at about 1000°c for a further day;

small quantities of coal are burned if necessary to maintain that temperature. Lastly, during their cooling stage, the bricks serve to preheat air for drying and combustion in the current firing zone.

Continuous tunnel kilns carry fuel economy to a very high pitch. The actual firing zone, where most of the gas or oil burners are, and where the temperature is highest, is at the middle. A steady supply of bricks, carried on cars, moves right through the tunnel from entrance to exit. In the opposite direction cool air moves from the exit toward the firing zone, flowing past bricks that have already reached their maximum firing temperature and cooling them. The air thus becomes hot, ready for more efficient combustion with the fuel when it reaches the firing zone. Hot air leaving the firing zone moves on toward the entrance, heating the dried bricks on their way to the firing zone. The kiln operates continuously for years at a stretch, and the temperature of various parts of its structure remains steady throughout. Once the structure has reached its correct temperature, that temperature has only to be maintained, which means a considerable saving of fuel. Further fuel-saving is effected by using some of the waste heat for drying and space-heating. Because a continuous tunnel kiln is not constantly being heated and cooled like an intermittent kiln, it is also less liable to structural deterioration.

Control of Firing Temperature

We have seen that when a brick is heated to about $1000°c$ a glassy bond begins to form, and that thereafter the pores in the brick are gradually eliminated. As the temperature continues to rise, more and more pores will be eliminated, making the brick denser and stronger—a process known as *vitrification*. In fact the brickmaker does not usually want a fully vitrified product; he wants a partially vitrified product, within the limits of porosity specified by his customers. If he does not raise the firing temperature high enough for long enough his bricks will be too porous; if he fires them at too high a temperature they will be too dense. The range of temperature between that which will produce just sufficient vitrification and that which will produce just too much is termed the *firing range*. The firing range for all ceramic articles varies with the chemical composition of the clay body, there being, in some cases, as little as 20°c between upper and lower limits, in others as much as 50° or even 100°c. But however wide or however narrow the firing range may be, the ceramist must always work within it. (In cases where complete vitrification is required, the firing range is that between the point at which full vitrification is achieved and that at which the body begins to *bloat*—i.e. develop an increasing internal porosity.) It is important that wares should not be heated too quickly, otherwise they will crack; they will also crack if cooling is too rapid after firing. Means of assessing and controlling temperatures the whole time ceramic articles are in the kiln are therefore essential.

The whole idea that temperatures can be measured against a fixed scale and expressed in numerical terms dates back only to the 17th century, when scientists first showed that mercury expands in equal increments with equal increments of heat. Before that (and indeed for long afterwards, since mercury-filled glass thermometers are unsuited to the measurement of temperatures as high as those encountered in a kiln) the ceramist had to equate temperature increases with changes of color. The marks on what we might call his mental thermometer were: barely visible red, dull red, various increasingly bright shades of red, yellow, and white, the lowest mark corresponding with what we should now call about 430°c, the highest with about 1160°c. In the hands of a

Automatic sequence control in this modern plant makes it possible for one man to control the whole process of material preparation, blending, forming, and firing on two production lines with a total output of 12,000 bricks per hour.

A series of three pyrometric cones, showing one squatting. These ceramic cones soften and bend over (squat) at different temperatures, depending upon their different compositions, normally at intervals of 30°C. Placed in the kiln, therefore, they provide a kind of visual thermometer for measuring the effects of increased temperature on different clay bodies during firing.

conscientious, experienced craftsman with a good color sense the system worked well; in the hands of a man without these qualities it could lead to a high proportion of spoiled products.

From the late 18th century onward several more objective, and therefore more reliable, standards became available. Josiah Wedgwood, for example, made and used a device based on the fact that clay contracts when heated, and that the amount of contraction can be measured against a simple linear scale. A century or so later the German ceramist Seger invented pyrometric cones, which are still widely used today. They consist of a series of three-sided pyramids, each made of a different ceramic body with a different known melting point, graded so that each will "squat," or slump over, at a temperature of about 20° to 30°c below that of the next (and more refractory) cone in the series. The higher the squatting temperature of a cone the higher its number in the series. Cones used in continental Europe are still known as *Seger cones*, the slightly modified cones used in America are called *Orton cones*, and those used in England— also slightly modified—are called *Staffordshire cones*.

The ceramist mounts several successively numbered cones—the one with the highest number having a melting-point close to that of the body he is firing—on a plaque in the kiln, where they can be observed through a peephole. As each successive cone slumps over it indicates that his own wares are approaching nearer and nearer to their melting point. Pyrometric cones are not only a

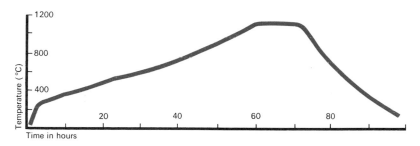

Schedule for firing bricks in a continuous tunnel kiln with a preheating (and oxidizing) zone of about 60 m., a firing zone of about 25 m., and a cooling zone of about 35 m.

guide to temperature, but also a guide to the effects of time and temperature taken together—that is to say, a cone suddenly and momentarily subjected to its melting temperature would not melt immediately, whereas a cone of precisely the same composition raised slowly to the same temperature would melt.

The ever-growing use of continuous tunnel kilns now means that more and more ceramic articles are being fired faster than ever they were in the past. Bricks that remained in clamps or intermittent kilns for several weeks are now in and out of a tunnel kiln within a matter of a few days, and comparable time savings are also effected in other branches of the ceramics industry. But as we have seen, faster heating and faster cooling increases the risk of cracking. To avoid this danger it is imperative to employ improved methods of temperature measurement. Today thermoelectric pyrometers (thermocouples that generate currents proportionate to temperature, the magnitude of the current being registered on a galvanometer), as well as optical and other types of pyrometer, are used for the precise measurement and recording of temperatures throughout the kiln. In this way the ceramist can keep track of time against temperature, from the time heating starts to the time when cooling is complete, without being dependent on pyrometric cones. Such a time-temperature graph is known as a *firing curve*.

2 Potter and Clay

The potter has certainly existed at least as long as civilization, and much of our knowledge of prehistory derives from the clay he fashioned and fired before written records began. To the archaeologist, shards of pottery reveal something of the level of craftsmanship and artistic development in Neolithic lake settlements; vases holding provisions for the dead tell of the burial customs, and the belief in an afterlife, of the Egyptians of 5000 B.C.; terra-cotta figurines suggest the appearance, artistry, and sense of humor of the Toltecs, who flourished in Mexico before the time of the Aztecs. In Mesopotamia written history itself was for many centuries set down in cuneiform scripts on tablets of clay; and on ancient Greek vases the potter-artist vividly recorded contemporary life and fashion.

The first brickmaker could make some kind of substitute for natural building stones by merely molding wet clay and drying it to temporary hardness. The first potter could not make any. worthwhile substitute for natural containers, such as seashells,

A 16th-century German stoneware jug.
Stoneware, which contains little or no
china clay but a high proportion of
ball or other plastic clays, is less
porous than earthenware and generally
less vitrified than china.

animal skulls, and gourd skins, until he fired the dried clay to permanent hardness; an unfired vessel would be too weak to hold any considerable weight of dry material such as grain, and utterly useless as a container for liquids. Provided a vessel is strong and permanently hard, however, it need not necessarily be impermeable. A pot that allows a little water to percolate through its walls is better than no pot at all, and in certain circumstances it may even be better than a nonporous one. In hot climates, for instance, evaporation from the outer surface of a porous vessel helps to keep the stored water or wine pleasantly cool.

Vessels of this kind can be made from not-very-refined clays fired to something between 900° and 1000°C—a temperature that produces just enough glassy material to hold all the particles firmly together. Such porous, unglazed, and comparatively coarse ware, varying in color from yellow to a reddish brown, is known as terra-cotta, and, while it is still used today in the manufacture of flowerpots, garden ornaments, and some building materials, it can be taken as representing perhaps the oldest type of product the potter ever made.

In this chapter, which is concerned essentially with the production of modern tableware, sanitary ware, and wall tiles, it is neither possible nor necessary to attempt to trace the history of pottery. But it is certain that early clay vessels left much to be desired; and although there was an infinite number of ways of improving on them, only a few broad principles were of outstanding importance. The first potters used clay very much as they found it. Since natural clays are of highly variable composition, such raw materials could not be relied on to behave in anything like a uniform way during shaping, drying, and firing; nor could they be guaranteed to give finished wares of predictable quality. One important line of advance, obvious in retrospect though probably not so in the beginning, was to select, blend, and purify clays, and mix other ingredients with them, to produce bodies with better controlled and more nearly constant properties. By Roman times progress along these lines had reached such a pitch that Samian ware, produced in widely scattered parts of the Empire, showed little or no appreciable difference in the composition of its reddish-brown body from one place to another. Strict control of body composition is still one of the ceramist's prime concerns, and he calls on any resources of science and technology that can help him to achieve it.

Another defect of primitive pottery was its permeability, a quality that may be desirable in storage vessels for tropical use but is certainly not so in drinking cups and vases. Permeability in a ceramic vessel is due to porosity of a particular kind. Internal pores, completely surrounded by dense material, do not make a vessel permeable; and neither do pores that open out onto one surface but are closed everywhere else. A pore system that results in permeability must stretch uninterruptedly from the internal surface to the external surface, the interconnected pores acting as capillary tubes. There are therefore two practicable ways of making a ceramic vessel impermeable. One is to seal by means of glazing all pores that reach the surface; in that case the vessel will become permeable again if the glaze surface is damaged. A better method is to fire the ware to a temperature at which it becomes fully vitrified, so that such pores as remain (commonly 5–10 per cent) are closed, thus making the body impermeable. Closed and open pores together constitute the *true* porosity of a body. The open pores constitute the *apparent* porosity, which can be measured by the absorption of liquid, and which gives rise to permeability. When porosity figures are quoted for a ceramic body (as they will be in this chapter), they normally refer only to apparent porosity. A glaze layer applied to a

"Porosity" is defined as the proportion of air spaces or voids between solid particles of a given material: Types of void shown here are sealed (A), channel (B), and pocket (C), and micropores (D), which are too small to admit water. "Permeability" is used to describe the existence of interconnected pores (E) that stretch uninterruptedly from one surface to the other.

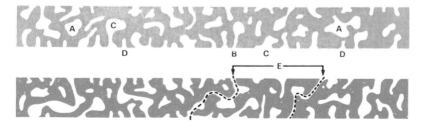

Examples of early ceramic work. Top row, left to right: Burial urn found in Wiltshire, England, of unglazed unrefined clay and dated c. 1400 B.C.; inscribed sun-baked clay tablet from Babylon, sixth century B.C., describing the capture of Jerusalem by Nebuchadnezzar in 597 B.C.; Greek vase with black design painted on reddish-brown body, c. 540 B.C.; Roman Samianware bowl, first or second century B.C.; similar reddish-brown ware was made throughout the Roman Empire.
Left: Toltec figure modeled in clay, A.D. 900–1100, found in Mexico.
Right: Dutch earthenware plate with heavy white glaze, chipped to reveal buff-colored body; made in Delft in the 17th century.

permeable body improves the surface, increases the strength, and renders it impermeable. Applied to an impermeable body it still has the first two functions but not, of course, the third. Impermeable bodies with little or no apparent porosity are usually referred to as being *nonporous*.

Vessels with porous bodies rendered impermeable by glazing were made in Egypt as long ago as the third millennium B.C. The first nonporous pottery, which later came to be known in the West as porcelain, was made in China more than 13 centuries ago. Much of it was not only fully vitrified but also glazed. Today we can still classify nearly all household ceramics as either porous and glazed or vitrified and glazed. Under the first heading comes earthenware; under the second come bone china and porcelain, feldspathic china, and vitreous sanitary ware.

Earthenware

Some dictionaries define earthenware as "ware made of clay, earth, and the like." The French, in fact, use one word—*faience*—to cover all such ware, irrespective of the color of the body, provided only that it is porous and glazed. The English word *earthenware* has come to have a more restricted meaning, being used to describe only white or cream bodies that are porous and covered with a transparent glaze. The change-over in earthenware from reddish-brown or gray to white or cream bodies came about with the first exploitation of the china clay deposits of Cornwall, at the beginning of the 18th century. Such clay, mixed with more plastic ball clays, flint, and feldspar, produced earthenware bodies that were not only whiter but also stronger than their predecessors. Soon after the middle of the century, Josiah Wedgwood's factory in Staffordshire was turning out high-quality white and ivory earthenware on a large scale, and by the early 19th century many manufacturers in Europe had followed suit. From then on, older forms of glazed porous pottery, such as *majolica* (gray or red-brown body with white opaque glaze), steadily lost ground, and they now constitute only a small fraction of the total output of domestic pottery.

Modern earthenware bodies are made mainly of lean china clays, more plastic ball clays, flint, and feldspar (though for earthenware bodies, just as for porcelain and china, a wider range of materials is now coming into use, including such mineral substances as wollastonite, talc, lime, and nepheline syenite). It is worth noting that *flint*, in its European sense, is a fine form of crystalline silica made of ground flint pebbles found in chalk beds; in its American sense it is very finely ground quartz sand. In England feldspar is commonly introduced into ceramic bodies in the form of Cornish stone, which is geologically intermediate between granite and clay, and consists mainly of feldspar, mica, and quartz. There is no single recipe for all earthenware bodies, just as there is no single recipe for all types of steel. Much depends on the thickness of the articles the ceramist is making, the texture and degree of porosity he requires, the firing temperature he intends to employ, and the price range of his finished goods. However, the following is typical of the composition of English earthenware bodies used in the production of tableware:

	percentage by weight
Mixed ball clays	26
Mixed china clays	26
Cornish stone	18
Calcined flint	30

Of the four main ingredients, ball clay renders the body plastic and workable during shaping and gives it sufficient strength when dried; china clay is mainly responsible for the whiteness of the body; Cornish stone or feldspar serves as a flux and a glass-forming agent; and flint makes for easier drying and reduces shrinkage during both drying and firing. More important, flint also enables the thermal expansion of the body to be raised sufficiently for it to be glazed with a glaze that will fit well. Most earthenware bodies, fired at a temperature of about 1150°c, have a porosity of 10 to 15 per cent.

In some earthenware-like bodies used in the production of wall tiles in the United States, feldspar is often partly or even entirely replaced by talc, which lessens the expansion of the finished tiles when their unglazed surface comes into contact with, and adsorbs, moisture. If such bodies contain approximately equal quantities of clay and talc they have a very small firing range. If the talc content is small (considerably less, say, than the clay content) the

body will not become sufficiently dense when fired to a temperature of about 1150°c. For these reasons talc may constitute
nearly 40 per cent of the body composition, clay (of which nearly
four fifths may be kaolin and rather more than one fifth ball clay)
accounting for nearly 30 per cent, and flint for the remainder.
Modern British wall tiles often include up to 8 per cent or so of
lime, which widens the firing range and allows far more accurate
size control of the fired tiles than if a conventional earthenware
body were used. Wall tiles are far more porous than earthenware
tableware, commonly having a porosity of 25 to 30 per cent.

Porcelain and China

The origins of all the white, vitrified, nonporous bodies now
used for tableware and sanitary ware can be traced to the great
impact that Chinese porcelain made on the aesthetic sensibilities
of the late Middle Ages, and to Western efforts at producing
materials with similar properties. The first pieces of Chinese
porcelain to reach Europe (where their hardness, whiteness, and
translucency aroused so much admiration) were brought in by
Arab merchants during the 12th century. It was not until more
than a century later that Marco Polo was able to reveal where
they were made, and not until the beginning of the 18th century
that a German alchemist and ceramist named Johann Friedrich
Böttger (1682–1719) first succeeded in making anything similar
in the Western World.

Far left: Wedgwood dish of cream-colored earthenware with transparent glaze, c. 1770; exploitation of Cornish china clays in the early 18th century made such white and cream bodies possible. Center: Chinese porcelain bowl with blue underglaze design, probably 14th century. The whiteness and hardness of Chinese porcelain was largely due to the nature of china clay deposits; discovery of similar deposits in Europe in the early 18th century made similar ware possible, such as this Sèvres porcelain teapot, 1757 (right).

The whiteness and hardness of Chinese porcelain depended largely on the whiteness of its major ingredient (china clay), and it was mainly because he found a source of china clay in Germany that Böttger succeeded where so many others had failed. European porcelain, of which Germany long remained the biggest producer, consists of about 50 per cent china clay, little or no plastic clay, varying proportions of feldspar, or feldspar-bearing minerals, and quartz. Many china clays are very lean and difficult to shape, so a small proportion of more plastic white-burning clay is sometimes included to facilitate shaping and to add strength to the wares before they are fired. Where no ball clay is included some of the china clays chosen must be of more than usual plasticity. The feldspar in the body melts comparatively early in the firing process, and at 100° to 200° before the peak temperature of 1300° to 1400°c is reached it gradually begins to dissolve other materials, eventually forming a fully vitrified, white, translucent material, consisting of crystals of mullite, quartz, and perhaps cristobalite, bonded together with glass, which may account for as much as 40 per cent of the total weight.

While it is true that continental European porcelain owes its whiteness largely to its china clay content, it is also true that the raw materials of porcelain almost invariably contain iron oxide impurities that could impair the whiteness of the fired body, leaving it cream. In the early German porcelain factories the problem was possibly overcome by accident. The intermittent coal-fired kilns of the time commonly produced an atmosphere deficient in oxygen, in which the iron oxide was reduced and hence caused no undesirable discoloration. At that time Priestley had not yet isolated the gas that Lavoisier later named *oxygen*, so it is very difficult to see how anybody could then possibly recognize that the atmosphere in the porcelain-firing kiln was reducing, as opposed to oxidizing. Later, when the nature of the kiln atmosphere was understood, the business of firing in a reducing atmosphere came to be part of the general mystique that surrounded the making of European porcelain. American ceramists call all vitrified whiteware for domestic use *china*, and all for industrial use *porcelain*. Since this chapter is concerned only with products for use in and about the home the semantic difference is unlikely to raise difficulties. In fact all white, vitrified ware, including vitreous china sanitary ware, American household and domestic china, Italian and Dutch vitreous china tableware, and English bone china, have characteristics broadly similar to those of European porcelain. Though they differ in body composition and—because they contain more fluxes or different fluxes—are fired at lower temperatures than European porcelain, they are all mechanically strong, all white, all almost nonporous (none commonly exceeding one per cent apparent porosity, and good-quality ware having virtually no porosity), and all have varying degrees of translucency. In all of them, with the exception of bone china, the major ingredient is china clay or kaolin, the others being white-burning ball clays, quartz or flint, and feldspar or some mineral rich in feldspar, such as Cornish stone or pegmatite.

In bone china, developed by Josiah Spode (1754–1827) in the early years of the 19th century, the main ingredients are bone ash, china clay, and Cornish stone. The bone ash is made from calcined cattle bones, the calcining being necessary to burn out the organic matter such as gelatine; what remains is essentially calcium phosphate. Since calcined bone ash, unlike quartz or flint, is slightly plastic, a bone china body usually needs no ball clay to make it sufficiently plastic for shaping. In firing, the Cornish stone and bone ash together act as a strong flux, and the bone ash makes the fired ware highly translucent. The proportions of clay, bone ash, and Cornish stone in a bone china body can vary a little, but the following recipe is typical:

	percentage by weight
Bone ash	52
Cornish stone	24
China clay	24

Sometimes a small amount of white-burning ball clay replaces some of the china clay. Bone china when fired consists of crystals of calcium phosphate, anorthite (a calcium aluminosilicate), and calcium silicate, all bonded together with a glass. This mineralogical composition is quite different from that of earthenware and porcelains, and it is this that gives bone china its high degree of whiteness and translucency, and makes it the strongest of all tableware bodies.

Stoneware

Although by far the greater part of modern tableware is made of either earthenware or china, some is of fine stoneware. The drainage and sanitation of most homes is also largely dependent on drainpipes and sewer pipes of coarser stoneware. Stoneware is less porous than earthenware, and generally less vitrified than china. Unlike either it is usually buff, brown, gray, or blue-gray rather than white; also unlike either it usually contains little or no china clay but a very high proportion of ball clays or other plastic clays. Particularly suitable are clays that contain a sufficiency of fluxes such as mica to enable the body to densify at a temperature somewhere between 1150° and 1250°c. Sometimes other fluxes are added, such as lime (used in small quantities, since too much of it can seriously reduce the firing range and so increase the risk of deformation during firing), talc, or magnesia. The two latter both have the effect of reducing the thermal expansion of the fired ware, so making it less liable to crack when subjected to sudden temperature changes.

Potters in western Germany began producing stoneware jugs and vases about 800 years ago, and from the 16th to the mid-18th century fine stoneware accounted for much of the tableware produced in western Europe. With the development of modern earthenware and china, however, its use in that context sharply declined, and from the mid-19th century onward it has been employed mainly in the production of far heavier goods, such as sewer pipes. By firing at a high enough temperature it is possible to make stoneware almost completely nonporous, but as the firing temperature is increased, so is the risk of deformation, particularly with heavy articles. For such articles it is therefore not uncommon to accept a certain degree of porosity, thus cutting down the cost arising from spoiled goods. (In Britain, although specifications allow up to 6 per cent for pipes having a wall thickness of 1.5 cm., and up to 10 per cent for those twice as thick, porosities are commonly considerably lower.) Porous drainpipes are still often salt-glazed, a process that is unique among glazing processes and will be briefly described in Chapter 3. Today, however, it is becoming increasingly common either to glaze stoneware pipes in much the same way as other ceramic wares or not to glaze them at all, having fired them at a temperature high enough to render them sufficiently impermeable.

Preparation of Bodies

It is a mistake to suppose that the distinctions between earthenware, stoneware, and china or porcelain are clear-cut and absolute. The most highly vitrified articles in one category tend to differ little in their main characteristics from the least highly vitrified articles in the next. And although different categories show differences in ingredients and processing, there are also a number of ingredients and methods of processing that they share in common.

First, they all contain nonplastic ingredients such as flint or quartz, and mineral fluxes such as Cornish stone or feldspar, as well as clays of varying degrees of plasticity. All these ingredients must be homogeneously mixed to ensure that the body will have uniform physical and chemical properties throughout. The nonplastic materials must therefore first be reduced to very small particle size; and either during or after grinding, metallic iron and iron-bearing contaminants that would cause dark spots in the fired ware must be removed by powerful magnets. The clay must be brought into such a condition that it can mix intimately with the finely ground nonplastic materials.

Vibro-energy mills used for processing ceramic materials. Each mill consists of a ring-shaped grinding chamber filled with suitable grinding media (usually sintered alumina cylinders), and the material occupies the spaces between the media. The chamber and its contents are then subjected to three-dimensional high-frequency vibration by means of a motor in the center tube.

Flint is usually first calcined (that is, broken down by heating the flint pebbles to red heat) and then ground. Sand, feldspar, or Cornish stone are wet-ground without preliminary calcining. Such materials were formerly ground in stone pans, not unlike those once used for grinding corn. Today these have been replaced by rotating ball mills, Hardinge conical mills, or vibro-energy mills. A rotating ball mill consists of a steel cylinder, often from two to three meters in diameter, that may be lined with blocks made of hard siliceous rock, with rubber, or with porcelain. In it are a great number of flint pebbles, alumina balls, or in some cases porcelain balls. The flint, stone, or feldspar, mixed with water, is introduced into the cylinder, and as it rotates, the mixture is repeatedly lifted and dropped together with the pebbles, whose impact gradually reduces it to finer and finer particles. The process may take many hours. Vibro-energy mills are essentially ball mills that vibrate rapidly instead of rotating. They speed up the process and also enable materials to be ground more finely than in any rotating ball mill.

The Hardinge conical mill differs from a rotating ball mill mainly in two ways. Whereas the ball mill must stop while each

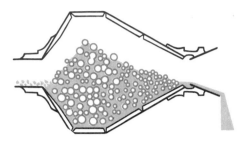 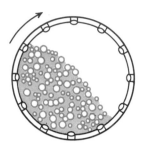

Action of the Hardinge continuous mill. During rotation, the conical shape segregates the material so that smaller particles move automatically to the discharge end and large particles automatically remain at the area of maximum diameter, until they are ground smaller, making continuous operation possible. Right: Cross section shows the cascade caused by rotation.

load of ground material is removed and a new load of unground material introduced, the Hardinge mill operates continuously, the material being introduced at one end and automatically discharged from the other while the cone continues to rotate. Because the container is conical instead of cylindrical, the grinding proceeds in a graduated, rather than a purely repetitive, way. As the cone rotates, its peripheral speed is highest at the loading end, where its diameter is greatest; there the biggest pebbles or balls collect and drop with the greatest impact. Toward the narrow discharge end the peripheral speed decreases; there, smaller pebbles collect and drop onto the partially ground material with a smaller impact. This graduated grinding helps to produce uniformity of particle size.

Particle size is of vital importance. In the case of flint, for example, it seriously affects shrinkage during drying and firing, the smaller the particles the greater being the shrinkage. The particle size of flint has two other effects. First, the finer it is the more readily the body vitrifies. Also, the fineness of the flint affects the rate at which quartz either is dissolved in the body or can convert into other crystalline forms, such as cristobalite. Both latter considerations affect the thermal expansion of the fired wares. Feldspar is used as a flux and a glass-forming agent; if it is too coarsely ground it will not produce sufficient vitrification at the usual firing temperature of the body, while if it is too

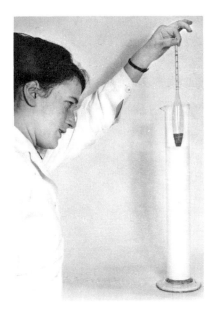

The sedimentation technique is the most common way of measuring particle size. A hydrometer is placed in a thoroughly stirred suspension of particles in water. As the particles (which are heavier than water) settle, the density of the suspension at the top of the cylinder decreases. As large particles settle faster than small ones, the change of density, read from the hydrometer, gives a measure of particle size distribution.

finely ground it will produce too much, increasing the risk of deformation in firing. The fineness of all nonplastic materials is therefore measured and controlled by a variety of techniques, the most common being sedimentation. In Britain the commonest method is to use a hydrometer in a tall cylinder containing a suspension of the particles in water. Since large particles settle faster than smaller ones, the density of the upper part of the cylinder steadily decreases. The hydrometer measures this density change and from the results of the readings it is possible to calculate the proportion of particles that are smaller than a given required size. Other and more sophisticated techniques that ceramists employ include measuring the lessening of light produced by suspensions of particles and measuring the permeability to air of dry compacts of ground materials. Ground quartz, flint, or feldspar is used in Britain with some 50 to 60 per cent of the particles by weight having a diameter of less than 10 microns. Clay particles are much finer still, particularly those of highly plastic clays.

The potter may grind his own nonplastic materials, but the

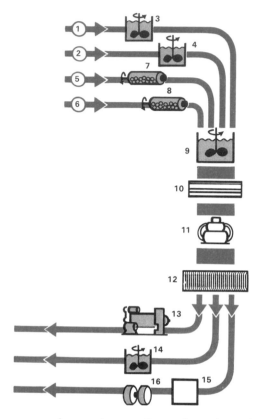

Preparation of clay bodies. Ball clay (1) and china clay (2) are each well dispersed in water in separate blungers (3 and 4). Quartz or flint (5) and feldspar (6) are separately ground in ball mills (7 and 8). Measured quantities of all four ingredients are next thoroughly mixed in the mixing ark (9) before going on to sieves (10) and the magnetic separator (11) that removes iron impurities, which would otherwise cause discoloration in firing. In the filter press (12) enough water is removed from the mixture to leave it in the form of plastic filter cakes. If the body is to be shaped plastically these go to the pug mill (13), which removes air bubbles and ensures homogeneity of mixture. Slip for slip casting (14) is prepared by mixing clay from the filter press with a small proportion of water and deflocculants. For powder-pressing, filter cakes are first partially dried (15), then ground, often in an edge-runner mill (16).

increasing tendency is to buy them ready ground from a miller, simply because grinding is usually more efficiently and economically done in large specialized plants. In America the miller commonly supplies such ingredients in powder form, while in Britain he frequently supplies them as *slips* (i.e., suspensions of particles in water). Clay, too, often reaches the pottery as a purified and blended mixture of controlled and constant properties. The clay supplier achieves such mixtures partly by carefully selecting and blending various clays, and he normally supplies them in shredded or powdered form rather than in plastic lumps.

The potter may ensure that his ingredients are finely ground and as consistent in properties as possible, but this will avail him nothing unless they are also thoroughly well mixed. Since many of the shaping processes he employs use clay in its plastic state, the least costly and least troublesome course would be to do his mixing in the plastic state, as the brickmaker usually does. Unfortunately this would seldom result in a mixture sufficiently intimate for his purpose (although stoneware bodies are sometimes made by plastic mixing). One course open to him is to mix all his ingredients dry, then add enough water to give the mixture the needed degree of plasticity. Another is to have each of the materials as a slip, then mix the slips, then extract enough water to leave the mixture plastic. The studio potter may use either method, but in the commercial production of whiteware for domestic use, only the second method, with certain variations, is normally employed.

In fact there is no one right way of mixing and no single universal mixing practice, but the following is probably the most widely used. Separate slips are prepared, one for each of the main ingredients (e.g. china clay, ball clay, feldspar, and flint), each slip being in its own *blunger*, a vessel in which rotating paddles keep the particles evenly distributed in suspension in the water. A typical scheme showing how the ingredients are later mixed in a mixing "ark," prior to preparing the body for shaping in various ways, is shown in the diagram on page 56. In some potteries the clays are prepared in slip form, the ready-ground nonplastic ingredients being added dry into the mixing ark. In that case all ingredients, including clays, are normally weighed and measured out dry. Where slips are prepared for all main ingredients, all are measured in slip form. Each slip is prepared so that it has a known weight per unit volume: For instance, each liter of flint slip may weigh 2 kg., made up of just over 1.2 kg. of dry flint and just under 0.8 kg. of water. The slips, of known content and gravity, are then measured out and mixed by volume.

Whichever mixing and measuring practice is adopted, the slip emerging from the mixing ark contains all the body ingredients in the required proportion. If the ware is to be shaped plastically, as most tableware is, this slip now goes to a filter press that will extract some water from it, but leave it plastic. The slip is pumped into chambers of suitable size, through holes cut in filter cloths, at a pressure of at least 7 kg/cm². This forces water out through the filter cloth, leaving behind a plastic "filter cake." For a typical earthenware body the filter cake will contain about 25 per cent water, as compared with the original slip that contained between 50 and 60 per cent.

The traditional filter press had wooden or metal frames to form the chambers, used cotton filter cloths, and had to be laboriously closed by hand before the slip was pumped in. The modern one is much bigger, has iron frames, and uses nylon filter cloths that, unlike cotton cloths, are not vulnerable to bacterial attack; it is closed automatically by hydraulic pressure. A typical modern press may hold between 3000 and 4000 kg. of clay at each loading.

The filter cake as it comes from the press is in no condition for immediate plastic shaping. For one thing it is wetter, and therefore more plastic, near the center than near the surface; for another, it contains air. Hence it must go to a de-airing pug mill (as described in Chapter 1), which consolidates it, gives it a

A typical filter press. The blended, sieved clay mixture is pumped under pressure into a series of compartments lined with nylon filter cloths. The water is forced through the fine mesh of the cloth at a pressure of about 7 kg/cm², leaving behind a thin square slab of plastic clay weighing about 40 kg.

uniform consistency, and at the same time removes the air. Not all shaping processes use clay in plastic form. For some it is needed in the form of a damp powder, and for others in slip form. Slip casting, which will be described later, depends on the ability of a plaster mold to absorb water from the clay slip in contact with it, so that a wall of fairly dry clay gradually builds up against its internal surface. A slip containing such a high proportion of water as the original body slip in the mixing ark (perhaps 50 to 60 per cent) would never build up to a sufficient wall thickness for, say, heavy sanitary ware, and when only such watery slips were available these wares could be made only by the slow and laborious method of handmolding from plastic bodies. To overcome this problem the ceramist now takes advantage of a process called *deflocculation*.

Clay particles, as we have seen, are like flat plates. On the face of each plate there are negative charges, and on the edges positive charges. Under neutral conditions, as when clay is suspended in

Passing filter cakes through the pug mill. The compressed clay, from which all bubbles of air have been removed, is then extruded as a column, which is then cut into suitable lengths for use.

The principle of deflocculation. Left: Under neutral conditions the plate-like particles in a clay-water mixture are mutually attracted in a face-to-face "card-pack" structure. Right: Addition of an alkaline electrolyte (deflocculant) produces a looser "card-house" structure among the now negatively charged particles, so that the system becomes more fluid.

water, the particles attract each other, and thus attach together in a large loose group that is electrically neutral. When an alkaline electrolyte is introduced into the water, however, the positive charges (H+) on the edges of the clay particles are balanced by the negative hydroxyl (OH−) charges in the water. Thus the particles are each now negatively charged, and because like charges repel, they move apart from each other, or *deflocculate*, so that the whole clay-water system becomes more fluid. This means that clay mixed with a little water and a very small proportion of some alkaline deflocculant such as sodium carbonate or sodium silicate will flow as readily as clay mixed with a great deal more water and no deflocculant. If too much deflocculant is added, the slip will become viscous again. The exact proportion of deflocculant required to produce the maximum counteraction of electrical attraction between the clay particles depends on several factors. It will be more, for instance, for plastic ball clays than for lean china clays, less for clays containing such alkaline impurities as lime than for clays not containing such impurities. On average, however, it is about 0.1 per cent. The use of alkaline deflocculants makes it possible to cast with slips that, while almost as fluid as the original body slip, have a water content of only about 25 per cent—little more than that of the plastic filter cake. Deflocculated slips are in fact prepared from cakes straight from the filter press by adding a very little water and, of course, deflocculants.

The fluid properties of a deflocculated slip are determined in part by the proportion of solids present in it but chiefly by the nature and amount of the deflocculants added—and slips are extremely sensitive to deflocculants. A slip flows most freely immediately after it is well stirred; if it is left unstirred for a short time its viscosity rapidly increases, though it will return to its original fluidity when re-stirred. This change of viscosity with time is called *thixotropy*. Besides this change, which can be reversed by stirring, deflocculated slips also have an irreversible change known as *aging*, during which they usually become more fluid and less thixotropic. For many slips several days may be needed before stable fluid properties are achieved. For this reason it is common practice to hold a large stock of casting slip and to draw on it only when it has aged sufficiently.

The commonest instrument used for testing the fluid properties of a slip is the *torsion viscometer*, in which a metal cylinder is allowed to rotate in the slip and the resistance to its motion is measured by the torsion of a long, fine wire attached to it. One reading, of course, simply gives the viscosity of the slip. To obtain a value for its thixotropy, the viscosity is first measured when the slip is in its most fluid state, immediately after thorough stirring; a second measurement is made after the slip has been allowed to stand undisturbed for one minute. The increase in viscosity is a measure of the thixotropy.

Control of the fluid properties of the slip is very important for successful casting. So far as viscosity is concerned, the slip must be fluid enough to enable it to run freely to all parts of the mold; but the most important property affecting the rate of casting (i.e. the rate at which the solid clay builds up on the mold wall) is thixotropy. All other things being equal, the higher the thixotropy the higher the casting rate, and therefore this is the property that has to be controlled more accurately than anything else. Slips with very high thixotropies, however, are unsatisfactory—not because they cast too fast, but because the resulting cast contains too much water, and will tend to be flabby on being removed from the mold. The exact values of thixotropies and fluidity for ideal casting vary widely, depending on the nature of the body and the kind of articles to be produced.

In controlling casting slip in a factory the usual practice is to start with a body containing rather less deflocculant than necessary, thus producing a more viscous and more thixotropic slip than is actually needed; very small quantities of deflocculant are then added until the desired values are reached. If too much deflocculant is introduced at the start, the only way to correct the situation is to add more plastic body to the system, and this will be difficult and inconvenient because of the aging characteristics referred to earlier.

For wares such as wall tiles, which are produced by dust pressing, the preparation of the body for shaping usually begins with the drying of unpugged filter cakes until their water content is reduced from about 20 or 25 per cent to around 8 per cent. They are then ground to the required fine powder on edge-runner mills. This may sound straightforward enough but in fact it is a somewhat roundabout method. At first, while in the mixing ark, the body is in slip form; next, in the filter press, it is brought into a plastic condition; thirdly it is semidried and rendered hard; lastly it is ground to powder.

A more modern method, known as spray drying, shortens the sequence of events. The spray dryer consists of a cylindrical drum, perhaps 3 m. in diameter and 5 m. high, with a conical outlet at the bottom; the whole structure is kept heated. The body

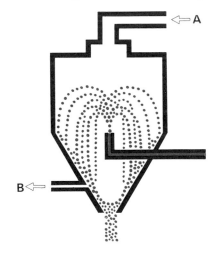

Action of a typical spray drier. Slip is pumped vertically in a fountain-like spray through the nozzle atomizer in the center of the chamber. It is then dried by hot air entering the chamber at A and leaving at B. By this means a body in slip form can be converted into an almost completely dry powder in one single operation.

in slip form, direct from the mixing ark, is sprayed into the dryer, either through a centrifugal atomizer near the top or through a nozzle atomizer pointing upward from near the bottom. Hot air drives out most of the water from the droplets of body slip, and what comes out from the bottom of the dryer is a nearly dry powder. How dry it is depends on the temperature in the dryer, the rate of feed, and the water content of the slip, but one or more of these factors can be regulated to ensure that the powder will in fact have the water content required.

Methods of Shaping

Given the body he needs in the form he needs it, the potter's next job is to shape it. Shaping methods that employ plastic bodies include hand modeling, hand molding, throwing, jollying or jiggering, plastic pressing, and extrusion. Of all these it seems certain that the oldest is hand modeling. In its simplest form it consists of making a *bat*, or disk of clay, to serve as the base of a vessel, and building the wall up on it by coiling long, thin rolls of clay one upon another. Only highly plastic clay lends itself well to the necessary rolling out and coiling, and since such clay cannot support any great weight before it is dried, the method is unsuitable for the making of very tall or very heavy vessels. Nevertheless it has been used successfully for many centuries by numerous native tribes of North America and southern Africa for small vases, dishes, and drinking vessels.

At the other extreme of hand modeling is ceramic sculpture, an art that calls for considerable innate artistic ability and long practice. However well pugged or well *wedged* (hand worked to eliminate air) his clay may be, the ceramic sculptor cannot be certain that it contains no *blebs* (air bubbles)—a risk that increases with the size and wall thickness of the article he is shaping. For large figures he may therefore include a small proportion of *grog* in the body. Grog is fired and ground refractory clay, which "opens" the body to which it is added, facilitating drying, allowing air to escape during plastic shaping, and reducing firing shrinkage. In order to keep down the wall thickness of a large figure, the ceramic sculptor may first shape it, next cut it into several pieces, then hollow out each piece, finally reassembling the pieces by exerting the minimum necessary manual pressure and using a slip of the same composition as the plastic body to make the joints good.

A piece of ceramic sculpture produced in this direct way, by modeling the clay, then drying and firing it, cannot be exactly reproduced. It is unique, and it is likely to be priced accordingly. The potter who wants to duplicate wares of similar aesthetic quality to sell at a lower price simply cannot work in that way. He must rely on either pressing or casting in a mold, of which the older process is pressing.

Shaping plastic clay in molds goes back at least to the time of the brickmakers of ancient Egypt, whose molds were simple wooden frames. The molds of complex and irregular shape that the studio potter now uses are invariably of plaster of paris, which absorbs moisture from the clay in immediate contact with it, thus making removal easy. The usual practice is to roll out a sheet of clay to the required thickness and press it firmly against the entire internal surface of the mold. Where the mold is in two or more parts (as it is, say, for a bust or a figurine), whatever clay remains above the rim of each part must be carefully trimmed off before they are all tied together. When the mold has absorbed sufficient water from the clay, its parts are gently prized away from each other and from the shaped clay. The last stage in the operation is to trim off any excess clay where the joint is ridged

Applying miniature details to china figures is intricate, exacting work and even today can be done only by hand.

Stages in throwing a simple pot on a potter's wheel. First the ball of soft clay is centered and worked into symmetrical form.

The clay is then opened out by pressing on the middle and supporting the sides.

The wall of the pot is then built up and made thinner by pressure between fingers and thumb.

The final in-out vertical curve is produced by pressing the fingers of one hand on the inside, and the palm and fingers of the other hand on the outside of the pot.

and to add clay wherever it is recessed, to give a flush finish. This again is essentially a slow process, and one calling for considerable skill. It is a way of duplicating complex shapes in clay, rather than a way of mass-producing them, and as such it is now used mainly by studio potters, and hardly at all in industrial manufacture. Yet hand molding can be regarded as the ancestor of those modern processes by which millions upon millions of wall tiles, cup handles, jug handles, and many other everyday necessities are now shaped from semidry or plastic clay in hand-operated or automatic presses that make use of dies and molds.

The traditional way of shaping pottery vessels of circular cross section was by *throwing* on the potter's wheel. This device of unknown origin, employed in all the Middle Eastern and Mediterranean civilizations of antiquity, proved so useful that the great majority of all pottery vessels were shaped on it until less than a century ago, though its use is now confined mainly to the small-scale production of artware. The photographs on page 65 show how the plastic clay is shaped by this method.

The throwing of a vase of exquisite design may be a fairly time-consuming operation, but this is far from being true of all throwing. Until fairly recent years many terra-cotta flowerpots, as well as a high proportion of food containers such as stoneware pickle jars and jam jars, were thrown on the potter's wheel. They were not works of art, certainly, but they had to be of standard capacity and standard shape. Some craftsmen could fashion such things on the wheel at the rate of one or even two a minute, keeping up the pace for nine or ten hours a day.

With the exception of teapots, coffeepots, and jugs, almost all earthenware tableware is now made by jollying and jiggering, though cups are sometimes made by casting, by turning on a lathe, or by plastic pressing. *Jollying* and *jiggering* are processes that utilize rotary motion to achieve symmetry, as does the potter's wheel, but they substitute molds and profiling tools for the craftsman-potter's hands and fingers. The two words are almost synonymous, but jollying is more commonly applied to the making of hollow ware, such as bowls, mugs, cups, and dishes, and jiggering, to making *flatware*—i.e. plates and saucers. In jollying, a mold is used to give the cup its external shape. A ball of

The jollying process. A ball of clay is placed in a rotating mold and a profiling tool is lowered to give the dish its internal shape, at the same time forcing the clay against the wall of the mold to give the external shape.

Making flatware on a roller plate-making machine. A bat, or disk, of clay is placed over a mold that shapes the face of the plate, while a profiled metal roller, rotating simultaneously with the mold, shapes the back.

clay of appropriate size is first put into a rotating mold and then a steel profiling tool, held on a movable arm, is brought into position. The tool forces the clay against the wall of the mold and simultaneously gives the cup its internal shape. Cup handles are made separately, most commonly either by pressing in plaster molds or by casting. With clay slip as an adhesive, they are then stuck onto the partly-dried cups before firing. In jiggering, the bat of clay is placed over a mold, which shapes the face of the plate or saucer, while the profiling tool shapes the underside as the mold rotates.

In early jollying and jiggering machines the profiling was controlled by hand. During the past 15 years or so many of the big pottery establishments have installed fully automatic machines, some of which utilize multiple jollying heads and also integrate shaping with partial drying. Such machines, calling for supervision by only one operative, are capable of turning out some 600 plates or 1200 cups per hour. A recent development is the replacement of the steel profiling tool by a profiled metal roller that rotates simultaneously with the mold. This has brought about even higher output rates, especially for plates, so that they too may now be produced at a rate of about 1200 per hour.

In one modern plate-making machine, clay is extruded from the pug mill through a circular die having a diameter less than that of the plates to be made; a pneumatically controlled wire cutter then slices the extruded clay cylinder into pieces thicker than required, so that the volume of clay is as needed. Each piece drops onto a mold carried by a moving belt, and each mold in turn is then automatically raised so that the piece of clay is pressed between the mold on which it rests and a heated metal die above. The die squeezes the clay so that it becomes thinner and covers the whole mold. The mold gives the precise shape of the face of the plate, while the die gives only the approximate shape of the back.

Finally the mold and partially shaped plate move along to come directly under a rotating jigger-tool or roller-head, which completes the shaping of the back. (The business of extruding the clay through a die of small diameter and cutting it into thick slices is largely a matter of convenience; it is also possible to produce bats of the required diameter and thickness, in which case the shaping can be done between two accurately formed molds, without the need for jiggering.) In some machines a moving belt carries the plates, still on the molds, to dryers, where they dry sufficiently to shrink away from the mold, ready for removal.

Extrusion

The only part extrusion from a pug mill plays in the making of tableware is in the production of plastic clay in the form of pugged rolls. It is never used for final shaping. However, stoneware drainpipes—except for traps and other difficult shapes, which have to be cast—are shaped entirely by extrusion. The process is an interesting one because such pipes are not of the same diameter over their entire length; the internal diameter of the socketed end must correspond with the external diameter of the unsocketed end, to allow for joining lengths of pipe as needed. The annular die from which the heavy stoneware body is extruded is designed to give a cylinder of plastic material of the wall thickness and diameter of the main pipe-length (which includes, of course, the unsocketed end). But when extrusion begins, this plastic cylinder strikes against a solid cup whose external shape and size correspond to the internal shape and size of the socket. The plasticity of the extruded body enables it to bulge out over the cup and take on the socket shape. The cup is then released, and extrusion continues without further hindrance until the rest of the required pipe-length, of smaller diameter than the socket, is complete.

In the 19th century, stoneware pipes made a tremendous contribution to the reform of urban sanitation. At that time they were commonly made in 70-cm. lengths on hand-operated machines, but much of the expense of laying such pipes is due to the time and labor involved in jointing, so that drainage and sanitary authorities naturally called for units of greater length. Since longer pipes necessarily meant heavier pipes, manufacturers could respond to the appeal only by installing automatic machines and replacing manhandling by mechanical handling. Today the manufacture of stoneware pipes is one of the most highly mechanized branches of the ceramics industry, and pipes of 15 cm. diameter are commonly made in 1-m. lengths, those of 30 cm. diameter in 2-m. lengths.

Slip Casting

So far we have looked only at plastic shaping processes, but some types of ware simply cannot be made—and certainly not economically made—from clay in its plastic state. An outstanding example is sanitary ware, now exclusively made by slip casting. The same process is also used in the production of ceramic figurines and almost any kind of whiteware of irregular shape, including many teapots, coffeepots, jugs, and vases.

Above: extruding a vitrified clay pipe from a fully automatic horizontal press. The method is described on page 69. Below: placing in the kiln a section of a 1-m.-diameter stoneware tower for concentrating nitric acid. The production of heavy stoneware for storing and processing acids and other corrosive liquids is an important part of the ceramics industry.

In its simplest form, slip casting begins with filling a plaster of paris mold with slip, pouring gently so that no air bubbles will be formed. As the mold absorbs more and more water from the slip, an even layer of clay gradually builds up over its entire internal surface. When this layer reaches the required thickness the slip that remains is poured off. The layer of clay in the mold must be left until it is dry enough and hard enough for removal. The period needed for drying the cast in the mold is usually much longer than the actual casting period. The total time required from pouring in the slip to removing the shaped article depends, as we have seen, on the fluid properties of the slip as well as on the size and wall thickness of the article. For a thin-walled jug or vase it may be a matter of minutes, for a closet several hours, and a thick kitchen sink may not be removed from the mold until the next day.

In fact articles of complex shape, such as washbasins, are not made by the simple kind of slip casting described above, which

Simple slip casting. Slip is poured into a plaster of paris mold (left), which absorbs water from the slip. A coating of clay is thus built up on the inner surface of the mold, the thickness of which depends on how long the slip remains in the mold. When the correct thickness is achieved, the surplus clay is drained off. While drying, the clay contracts, and can easily be removed from the mold (right).

gives wares a well-defined external shape but a less clearly defined internal shape. They are made by the double-wall casting method, in which slip is poured between two parts of a mold, one male and the other female. This ensures not only that both internal and external surface will be clearly defined but also that the wall thickness will be precisely as required. It also allows wall thickness to vary from one part of the article to another, which simple slip casting does not. Both plaster surfaces, of course, absorb water from the slip, and in order that a solid wall of clay will build up to full thickness between them it is necessary to keep the slip topped up during casting. While sanitary ware is still drying in the mold, or just afterwards, the holes needed for taps, pipes, and so on are cut in it. Large and complex articles cannot generally be cast whole. A closet and its trap, for instance, may be cast in several parts in separate molds. After removal

Assembling parts of a closet, which have been cast in separate molds, by sticking them together with clay slip.

from the molds the parts are assembled by sticking them together with clay slip—a logical though elaborate extension of the
age-old practice by which the potter fixes handles to cups and jugs.

The potter cannot cast good ware in poor molds, and the
making of good ones (some of which weigh several hundred kilograms) is a highly skilled task. Besides being of exact shape, molds
need to be hard and of consistent porosity, since they are quite
costly and must have a reasonably long life. For sanitary ware,
for instance, a mold may be expected to yield as many as a
hundred casts, though for intricately shaped artware, where
sharp definition of fine detail is essential, the ceramist will be
content with far fewer. To allow for drying and firing shrinkage
the mold must always be bigger than the ware to be shaped—
bigger by up to 15 per cent. Furthermore, since shrinkage,
especially of irregularly shaped articles, will not be equal in all

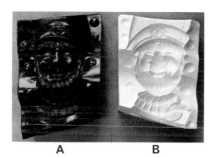

A   B

*Stages in making a ceramic figure by
molding. First a master figure is made
in epoxy resin (A) from which a plaster
of paris working mold (B) is made in
several interlocking parts. The clay
cast (C) made in this mold is then
dried and biscuit-fired (D), glazed and
glost-fired (E), decorated (F), and
enamel-fired (G). Note the shrinkage
between stages (C) and (D).*

C   D

E   F   G

directions, the mold must also be of different shape from the finished article. It is in making just the right allowances for these differences of size and shape that so much skill in design is called for. The master molds from which working molds are made were formerly of hard plaster, but today this material is being superseded by epoxy resins, which produce master molds with a much longer life.

After modeling, molding, throwing, jollying, or casting, there is always some finishing, or even further shaping, to be done. Surfaces that have been in contact with a mold, for instance, will be slightly rough, and may also show ridged mold marks. Such mold marks and other surface roughnesses are removed with a flat-bladed instrument called a *pallet*, then finally smoothed with a damp sponge before the ware is sent for drying. When flatware is completely dry, the edges are brought to the right profile with a shaped steel tool. This process, known as *fettling*, is now sometimes mechanized.

The shaping of wall tiles is wholly mechanized. The powdery body, moist enough to allow plastic deformation under pressure, is poured into an open mold consisting of a base, capable of movement in a vertical direction, set in a stout rectangular metal framework. Next a die descends onto the powder, exerting a pressure of several thousand kg/cm^2. The resulting compaction of the powder will be greater toward the edges, where its tendency to squeeze outward is resisted by the framework, than in the middle. To allow for this, a striking-off tool is used to ensure that when the mold is first filled the depth of powder is less in the middle than near the edges. If the downward pressure of the die were released while the base of the mold was still within its metal framework, the newly compacted body would spread out and jam in the framework. Instead, the mold is thrust upward out of the framework against the reduced, but still considerable, downward pressure of the die. Only then is the whole pressure of the top die released; the tile does then spread out slightly, and the bad edges must be removed by automatic fettling. Wall tiles usually measure either 10 cm. by 10 cm. or 15 cm. by 15 cm., and a modern fully automatic tile press, possibly shaping several tiles on one die, can press and fettle some 35 m^2 of tile per hour.

Drying and Firing

After shaping, by whatever process, the next operation is thorough drying, to ensure that no water remains in the ware to turn to steam and shatter it during firing. Since pottery is thinner than bricks, it can be dried faster; but the fact that a single pottery article may vary considerably in thickness from one part to another means that different parts may dry, and try to shrink, at different rates. This leads to stresses being set up that, if excessive, can cause cracking. The amateur ceramist often tackles the problem by loosely covering the thinner parts of his vessels with aluminum foil or a thin sheet of plastic material to retard their drying. The same practice is sometimes necessary in the commercial production of very large articles, but it is not practicable under mass-production conditions. The large-scale manufacturer must therefore find the maximum safe drying rate for each kind of article he makes.

A large modern tile factory in West Germany. A single fully automatic tile press, shaping several tiles in one die, can produce some 35 m² of tile per hour.

We saw in Chapter 1 that drying shrinkage takes place during the early stages of drying, and that once the water content of the ware falls below a certain critical level, drying continues without further shrinkage. Since wall tiles are pressed from semi-dry powder, their water content is very near, or even below, this critical level from the start, and the problem of shrinkage scarcely arises. Incidentally, wares shaped plastically or by slip casting have a sufficient moisture content to leave them subject to plastic deformation before drying, and must therefore be handled with great care. Wall tiles and other articles shaped by dry pressing are more robust at that stage.

Tableware is commonly dried while still in the mold, straight from the jollying or jiggering machine, and the dryer is supplied, wherever possible, with hot air from the kiln, which would otherwise be wasted. The humidity is high at first, when the risks arising from differential drying rates are greatest, and low later. The temperature is not allowed to exceed 60°C, since at a higher temperature the plaster mold would dehydrate and be ruined. Drying is often done in a vertical drying oven in which the wares move up one side and down the other, as shown in the diagram opposite. At the far side plates are removed from the mold, to go ahead for fettling, while the empty mold is left on the automatic conveyor in the dryer to return to the jiggering machine. For some kinds of ware—for instance, cups and some sanitary ware—drying can be accelerated by blowing a gentle jet of warm air into the article.

Once cast, sanitary ware must remain in the mold until it has dried sufficiently to become rigid enough for removal. Then, after finishing and fettling, it is usually placed on steam-heated racks or in a chamber dryer until its water content is down to less than 1 per cent. Such ware may also be dried in continuous tunnel dryers. Other methods of drying, of more limited and special application, include infrared and radio-frequency drying, and in certain cases articles may be dried by passing an electric current through them. Wall tiles, which present no serious drying problem, almost always go into tunnel dryers, loaded on the same truck that will eventually carry them through the tunnel kiln without further unloading and loading.

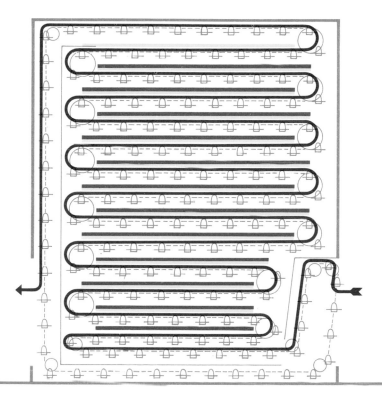

Above: sectional view of a modern
vertical drier, showing the path taken
by the tableware on the conveyor
belt, between hot-air jets (yellow) and
suction units (red). Right: This
vertical drying unit handles the output
of two semiautomatic platemaking
machines, each producing 12
medium-sized plates per minute.

What happens next after drying depends on the nature of the ware, and to some extent on local or national practice. Vitreous china sanitary ware is almost always coated with glaze while in the dry state and then fired once only, so that the body must vitrify at the same temperature as the glaze matures. Many wall tiles, some art pottery, and in America many less expensive cups, vases, and so on are treated in the same way. Stoneware pipes when dried are also sometimes treated similarly, but many are still salt-glazed during the course of firing itself. However, all better-class tableware, whether of earthenware, china, or porcelain, is first fired before the glaze is applied, a process known as *biscuit*, or *bisque*, firing.

Biscuit firing carries somewhat different meanings in different countries. In Britain and America it means firing to the temperature at which the body acquires the final degree of vitrification needed, usually between 1150° and 1200°c for earthenware, between 1200° and 1250°c for bone china and other household or hotel china. After the glaze is applied, the next firing, called the *glost* firing, is then carried out at a lower temperature—between 1050° and 1150°c. In continental Europe, however, the biscuit firing of porcelain is done at 800° to 900°c. This is considerably below the temperature needed for the ultimate degree of vitrification, but it is sufficient to break down the clay molecule and drive off the water content, and also to burn out any carbonaceous matter. Biscuit produced in this way is very fragile and porous; it is coated with glaze and fired again, the second firing being conducted at temperatures between 1400° and 1450°c, usually in a reducing atmosphere.

In this chapter what will be said about kilns and the setting of wares in the kiln applies only to the first firing process (though for wares that undergo only a single firing this is, of course, the only one). Glost firing as a separate operation is dealt with in Chapter 3. Kilns used for firing pottery, like those used for firing bricks, can be placed in two main categories, *intermittent* and *continuous*. Although the use of continuous kilns is constantly increasing, especially in large undertakings, it must be remembered that some tableware, in Europe at least, is still manufactured by numerous small potteries relying on older intermittent kilns, some of which burn coal. How the ware is *set*, or placed in the kiln, depends largely on the type of kiln, how high it is, and how clean or dirty the kiln atmosphere is. In coal-fired intermittent kilns the atmosphere will be contaminated with smoke and sulfur, from which the ware must be protected. Such protection is given by placing the pottery in *saggers*—boxes made of refractory fireclay and designed in various ways to hold articles of various shapes and sizes. Intermittent kilns are always considerably higher than continuous tunnel kilns, and in them 15 or 20 filled saggers may be stacked one on top of another, a procedure that not only involves a great deal of heavy lifting and ladder-climbing but also subjects the saggers to extremely heavy wear and tear.

The ceramist uses saggers only when he must. Quite apart from the fact that the initial cost and replacement cost are considerable, they take up a great deal of kiln space that he would rather give to the articles he is actually firing, and they also absorb a great deal of heat. In the clean atmosphere of a modern tunnel kiln they can be dispensed with. In the type of tunnel kiln, now rarely used in the production of domestic ware, that is both open-flame and fired with heavy oil, they are still needed, but in such cases they are loaded onto the tunnel cars in stacks of maybe seven or eight high, which at least cuts down lifting and eliminates ladder-climbing.

It is because of their low thermal efficiency and their high manpower demands that intermittent kilns have been largely replaced by tunnel kilns over the past three or four decades. These are essentially long brick tunnels about three meters high, a few meters wide, and usually between 50 and 100 m. long, though kilns used for firing sanitary ware are often longer. The bottom space of the tunnel is taken up by the wheels and structure of the kiln cars, and a comparatively cool sealed-off portion for the rails on which they run. In the tunnel, the temperature steadily increases from where the cold loaded trucks enter, reaches a maximum near the middle where the wares must attain their required firing temperature for several hours, and decreases again toward the exit, to allow the pieces to cool gradually and leave the kilns at little above room temperature. If such kilns are of

Loading a large gas-fired intermittent kiln. Continuous tunnel kilns have largely replaced intermittents in most modern tableware factories, but intermittents are still widely used, as shown here, for firing heavy insulator units.

Continuously fired tunnel kilns have taken the place of intermittent kilns during recent years because of their greater thermal efficiency and their suitability to continuous production methods. Left: loading a kiln car with ware for biscuit firing. Right: A loaded car begins its journey through the kiln.

the open-flame type they are fired with some clean-burning, sulfur-free fuel, such as natural gas, town gas, butane, propane, or kerosene. If producer gas or heavy oils are used and if, at the same time, wares are to be fired without saggers, it is necessary to have a *muffle* throughout the length of the kiln—that is, an inner chamber, heated from the outside, in which the wares do not come into contact with flames and products of combustion. Open-flame kilns are, in general, preferable to muffle kilns on two counts: They are thermally more efficient, and they give greater uniformity of temperature over the whole cross section of the kiln. Electric tunnel kilns, though they are successfully used for biscuit firing, are not very commonly so used, largely because it is difficult to produce heating elements that will withstand long continuous running at much above 1200°c; they are far more widely employed in decoration firing, which does not call for such high temperatures.

Although continuous tunnel kilns are a great advance on the

old types of intermittent kiln, they do have certain disadvantages. Once started, they normally remain in operation night and day, vacations included, for years at a stretch, unless they have to be brought to a standstill because of some near-catastrophe, such as the derailment of a tunnel car. This means that factory output must be geared to the demands of the kiln. Further, they allow only relatively small adjustments in the speed of operation, although quite big ones may be desirable due to the differing requirements of the various articles fired in them. What is more, they take up a great deal of factory space and involve high capital investment, so that the installation of an additional one is hardly a sound business proposition for the manufacturer who sees the opportunity of increasing his output by a few per cent but no more.

Efforts to overcome these drawbacks are sometimes made by using several short tunnel kilns of small cross section. This makes it possible to fire different articles at different rates, instead of firing all at the pace of the slowest. A more recent development, however, is the highly efficient modern intermittent kiln. Such kilns are frequently of the "top hat" type of construction. The description is apt, for not only does the main upper part of the kiln look like a top hat, but it can also be taken off and put on again by simply raising and lowering it. The kiln consists of two thick refractory bases set a short distance apart on the factory floor, of equal size and each measuring up to three meters across. One of them is loaded with wares ready to be fired, with not even a cover over them. The other base is also loaded, but the wares are completely covered over with the giant top hat that constitutes all but the base of the kiln, and they are then fired. Once the firing ends, the top hat, complete with its electric heating elements, gas burners, or oil burners, is mechanically raised, moved, and lowered onto the other refractory base, ready to begin the firing of the articles already loaded on it. In the older intermittent kilns it took a long time after firing for the atmo-

Opposite: a "top-hat" kiln loaded for firing. When firing ends, the top hat, complete with its heating elements, is mechanically raised, moved, and lowered onto another refractory base loaded ready for firing.

sphere to cool sufficiently for people to enter and begin unloading and loading. Here such delays are virtually nonexistent. Similar savings of time can be effected with other types of modern intermittent kilns in which one part of the kiln structure moves between two duplicate complementary parts on rails.

In any kiln with a clean atmosphere, as we have already seen, the ceramist saves valuable space by dispensing with saggers. He saves yet more by all kinds of ingenious setting practices. Some good examples are to be found in the firing of sanitary ware, which is more often than not carried out in single-deck tunnel kilns. If two closets, for instance, were simply stood side by side on the floor of the kiln car, there would be a very considerable waste of space between their narrow bases and some waste of space between their broad rims, but in fact a row of three can be placed so as to occupy little more room than a row of two. The two outer ones stand on the floor of the car while the middle one is raised up on a refractory stand, so that its rim overhangs the rims of the outer ones. Washbasins rest, back downward, on a long wedge of refractory material in such a way that they nest into one another with a minimum of space between.

Economizing on kiln space, however, is by no means the ceramist's only concern in setting. In the course of firing, his wares will temporarily soften and permanently shrink. Parts such as the trap of a closet must therefore be propped up to prevent the sagging and distortion that would otherwise occur when they softened. The base of a closet, like all the rest of it, will also soften and shrink. If it stands directly on the solid, unyielding floor of the car, not only will its freedom to shrink be impaired but it will also stick to the car floor. It therefore rests either on corrugated paper, which is free to contract as shrinkage occurs and which will leave only a little fine ash on the car floor, or else on a layer of some powdery refractory material (not sand, since very fine sand could bring the risk of silicosis).

When, less commonly, sanitary ware is fired in a double-deck tunnel kiln, the floor of the kiln car is likely to be loaded in much the same way as described above. However, a second deck is built up on the car by means of refractory props (uprights) and bats (flat sheets), to accommodate more articles. The time that

85

If heavy objects are placed in direct contact with the floor of the kiln car, this will cause deformation and cracking when the ware shrinks during firing. To avoid this, corrugated paper or, as here, polystyrene matting may be used; this will yield with the shrinking clay and gradually disintegrate during firing.

sanitary ware takes to go through the kiln varies, among other factors, with the cross section of the kiln and the density of setting of the ware, but it is likely to be somewhere between 15 and 25 hours, as compared with the 4 or 5 days that would be needed in the old-fashioned intermittent kiln.

The setting of European porcelain tableware, which is biscuit-fired at a low temperature and glost-fired at a very high one, presents special problems. More will be said about the firing of European porcelain tableware in Chapter 3. What is said here applies to other kinds.

Plates are very often set in *bungs*—that is, they are piled one on top of another, separated only by a layer of refractory powder, the shape of the foot of the plate offering good support in the nesting. There is a limit to the weight that the plates near the bottom of the pile can support, so the bungs must not be excessively high. Where precision of shape is of special importance, each plate is supported in its own carefully shaped refractory setter, the setters being fitted with short feet so that they can be stacked one on another—setter, plate, setter, plate, and so on. If cups were placed higgledy-piggledy on the kiln car, the firing process would rob many of them of their precise round cross section. Instead they are fixed rim to rim with a little organic glue, which will burn out in the kiln; each then resists any tendency on the part of the other to become distorted in one direction during firing. Cups *boxed* in this way are stood up-

Plates and cups stacked on the kiln car ready for biscuit firing. To prevent them from moving and losing their true shape, the plates are piled on top of one another separated by layers of refractory powder, while cups and bowls are fixed rim to rim with organic glue, which burns out during firing.

right, and since their combined height is quite small, several decks are built up on the kiln car with props and bats to hold more.

For a reason that will be explained in the next chapter, wall tiles, which are glazed on one side only, need to be slightly concave. The necessary curvature of several thousandths of a centimeter is given to them during firing. On the kiln car a pile of flat tiles rests on a thick, refractory setter whose upper surface is accurately ground to the required concave shape. As the tiles soften in the kiln they drop to match its curvature.

Sanitary ware, tableware, and wall tiles are now fired almost entirely in either tunnel kilns or modern intermittent kilns with a clean atmosphere, and methods of setting vary little from one type of kiln to the other. Stoneware pipes, however, may be fired in any one of three widely differing types of kiln, and the type employed even has a direct bearing on how they are processed. The types of kiln used are older open-flame intermittents (usually burning heavy oil), continuous chamber kilns not unlike the Hoffman kilns used in firing Fletton bricks, and very large tunnel kilns, perhaps twice as wide as those used for tableware. In either of the first two, the pipes can be salt-glazed during firing or, of course, fired to impermeability so that glazing is not necessary. The growing practice of firing in tunnel kilns makes salt glazing not exactly impossible but extremely difficult. Pipes so fired must therefore have either an orthodox ceramic glaze or no glaze at all.

One very good reason for the increasing use of tunnel kilns for stoneware pipes is that they save time in firing. The time required in a tunnel kiln may be as little as 40 or 50 hours, while in an intermittent or continuous chamber kiln it is several times longer. Pipes are loaded onto the kiln cars narrow end down, socketed end up. To save much of the space that would otherwise be wasted due to the big difference between the diameters of the two ends, they are set alternately one low down, one raised, one low down, one raised. Small pipes are sometimes placed inside large ones, while traps and so on may simply lie on top. Each large pipe rests on a setting ring of its own narrow-end diameter, the ring being made of unfired stoneware of the same body as the pipes being fired. After firing, the setting rings have to be broken away from the pipes, but they are not wasted. Heavy stoneware bodies generally contain several per cent of grog, and old setting rings are broken and ground to provide it.

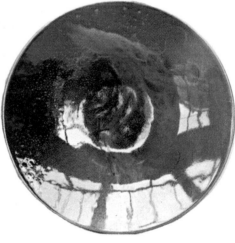

3 Glazing and Decorating

An orthodox ceramic glaze is a mixture of materials that when heated sufficiently will form a permanently hard layer of glass over a ceramic article, rendering a porous body impermeable or adding brilliance and smoothness to a body that is already virtually nonporous and impermeable. During firing, a glaze must reach just the degree of viscosity that will enable it to shape itself evenly over the surface of a ceramic article without running off edges and corners. The temperature at which it behaves in this way, producing a glass surface that is free from bubbles, pinholes, craters, and waviness, is called its *maturing* temperature. Ceramic articles treated in this way are described as *glost ware* and the process of firing is known as *glost firing*.

Glaze Composition and Classification

Glaze compositions vary enormously, the exact recipe depending on many considerations, including the thermal expansion required of the glaze, whether it is to be colorless or colored,

Color effects achieved by firing the same copper oxide glaze in two different atmospheres. Fired in an oxidizing atmosphere it gives the blue-green of the base of the vase and the left-hand side of the plate; fired in a reducing atmosphere it gives the brilliant red known as rouge flambé.

whether it is to be transparent or opaque, and the firing temperature at which it must mature and fuse with the body. Perhaps the only safe generalization is that all glaze mixes contain ingredients that will supply: (a) the amphoteric (neutral) oxide alumina; (b) silica, and often another acidic oxide, boric oxide; (c) some basic oxide or oxides (often three or four different ones) that will flux with the silica (and, where it is used, also with the boric oxide) to form a glassy material.

Before a glaze is fired, it must lie evenly over the surface of the ceramic article in the form of a fine homogenous powder. In general, the only practical way of achieving this is to mix all the powdered ingredients with water to form a slip that can be sprayed onto the ware, or into which it can be dipped. This implies that all the ingredients must be insoluble in water, since if it were only possible to use water-soluble ingredients, which is not the case, no such solution could give a sufficient density of glaze materials to produce a coating of the required thickness.

For glazes that must mature at temperatures of between 1020° and 1100°c (which includes those used for wall tiles and for all tableware other than that of European porcelain) it happens that some of the most widely used ingredients are, in fact, water-soluble in their raw state. Among the most important is borax, needed to provide boric oxide (B_2O_3), which has a powerful effect in reducing the fusing temperature. Such ingredients must first be rendered insoluble in water by a process called *fritting*, and all glazes that involve this process are known as fritted glazes. Glazes that must mature at temperatures in excess of about 1150°c (that is, those used for European porcelain tableware, vitreous china sanitary ware, and stoneware pipes) can be made entirely from ingredients that are insoluble in water to begin with; they therefore involve no fritting, and are known as *raw glazes*.

To make a frit that will supply a low-temperature glaze with boric oxide, water-soluble borax is mixed with other ingredients, such as Cornish stone, flint, feldspar, and sand, and strongly heated in an intermittent or continuous frit kiln, rather like a small glass tank. The heated mixture fuses to form a glass (the *frit*) consisting largely of silicates and borosilicates. As the hot glass frit flows from the kiln it is quenched in cold water so that it can later be milled to the particular particle size required. Other very widely used ingredients of low-temperature glazes are compounds containing lead oxides, which not only reduce the fusing temperature but also impart to the glaze a high refractivity, and thus a brilliance, not easily achieved in any other way. These, too, have to be fritted, though not for quite the same reason as boric oxide. At least one common compound containing both lead and oxygen seems at first sight to have all the qualities needed to make it suitable for adding directly to a glaze mix. This is white lead, $2PbCO_3.Pb(OH)_2$. Besides being insoluble in water it also has a flaky structure somewhat like that of clay, so that it stays well in suspension. Until the closing years of the 19th century it was, indeed, commonly used as a glaze ingredient. But unfortunately, like many other lead compounds, white lead is soluble in the weak hydrochloric acid present in human gastric juices. It could enter the noses and mouths of workers who

In preparing a fritted glaze, the appropriate ingredients are first heated in an intermittent or continuous frit kiln, rather like a small glass tank furnace. The typical oil-fired intermittent kiln shown here has a capacity of 1000 kg. and fires the frit at about 1300°C. As the hot frit flows from the kiln it is quenched in water and then milled to the required particle size for making the glaze slip.

handled it, eventually being dissolved in the digestive tract and causing lead poisoning; in a single year of the 1890s over 400 cases of lead poisoning in potteries were reported in Britain alone. And it should be remembered that the danger was only to the workers who handled such compounds, not to those who used the glazed ware.

Toward the turn of the century factory legislation did much to cut down the incidence of the disease by insisting on a variety of safety measures. These included the prohibition of eating, drinking, or smoking where dangerous lead compounds were in use, insistence on the wearing of respirators and protective clothing for certain jobs, and a complete ban on employing women and young people for such work. But exemption from certain safety measures was granted to potteries using only lead frits, which were considerably less soluble in weak hydrochloric acid than raw lead compounds. The early frits that came into use as a result were of lead monosilicate and lead bisilicate, produced by fritting lead oxides with sand. Although these were a big improvement they were nevertheless more soluble than was desirable, and some health precautions still remained necessary.

Over the years experiment and research resulted in further improvements, one of the most important discoveries being that the addition of a small proportion of alumina to such frits considerably reduces their acid-solubility. By 1950 the use of raw lead glazes was wholly prohibited in Britain, and the use of a standard lead bisilicate frit established. While this brings all the desirable qualities of lead to a glaze, it eliminates the danger of lead poisoning. The standard frit contains between 63 and 66 per cent by weight of litharge (PbO), between 2 and $3\frac{1}{2}$ per cent of alumina (Al_2O_3), and a sufficient percentage of silica (SiO_2) to bring the combined weight of litharge, alumina, and silica to not less than 98 per cent of the total weight of the frit. Several countries besides Britain have solved the problem in a similar way, but in some the use of raw lead compounds is still permitted under safeguards.

The composition of a fired glaze can be expressed in terms of the percentage by weight of the various oxides it contains, and the following shows the composition of an earthenware glaze maturing at a temperature somewhere in the region of 1050°C:

	percentage by weight
Silica (SiO$_2$)	36.0
Boric oxide (B$_2$O$_3$)	8.5
Alumina (Al$_2$O$_3$)	5.5
Lime (CaO)	3.0
Litharge (PbO)	44.0
Sodium oxide (Na$_2$O)	3.0

However, low-temperature glazes can be made without lead, often by increasing the boric oxide content. The composition of a leadless earthenware glaze, also intended for firing at 1050°C, might be as follows:

	percentage by weight
Silica (SiO$_2$)	54.5
Boric oxide (B$_2$O$_3$)	18.0
Alumina (Al$_2$O$_3$)	10.5
Lime (CaO)	8.5
Sodium oxide (Na$_2$O)	2.5
Potassium oxide (K$_2$O)	6.0

Some of the ingredients used in a glaze mix contribute to two or more oxides, so that a factory recipe usually looks very different from an analysis of the fired glaze. A particularly simple-looking one for a leadless glaze, with a maturing temperature of between 1040° and 1090°C, is 80 per cent by weight of a particular borosilicate frit plus 20 per cent of china clay. However, it has to be remembered that the frit itself is made from a mixture of borax, quartz, feldspar, chalk, and china clay. One recipe for a lead glaze of the same maturing temperature is 80 per cent lead-silicate frit, 12½ per cent china clay, 6 per cent quartz, and 1½ per cent feldspar.

Raw glazes, often called *feldspathic* glazes, mature at temperatures in excess of 1150°C, and are used for products that undergo only a single firing, such as vitreous china sanitary ware, as well as for European porcelain tableware, which is fired to full vitrification only after the glaze is applied. High glost-firing temperatures restrict the range of ingredients that can be used in the mix. Some ingredients of low-temperature glazes would make the glaze too fluid at temperatures above 1150°C; others, such as lead and borax, would volatilize. Among the most common ingredients of raw glazes are feldspar, sand or quartz, whiting (calcium carbonate), barytes (barium sulfate), and zinc oxide. A typical recipe is:

	percentage by weight
Feldspar	35
Quartz	30
Whiting	15
Clay	7
Zinc oxide	5
Barytes	5
Dolomite	3

All the glazes so far mentioned are colorless and transparent, of the kind nearly always used for tableware. Some products, such as sanitary ware, call for a brighter and white glaze, however, partly in order that the body of the articles, as a matter of technical convenience in manufacture, need not be so white as it would otherwise need to be. The whiteness of the glaze is normally achieved by adding several per cent of tin oxide. This, though thoroughly mixed with the other glaze ingredients, does not react with myriads of minute specks of white tin oxide embedded in it. The refractive index of the tin oxide is very different from that of the glass, so that the passage of light through the glass is blocked, making it opaque. Tin oxide, used in white glazes for many centuries, is very expensive. Today it is often replaced by two or three times the quantity of cheaper zirconium silicate, either raw or in the form of a high-temperature zircon frit.

Colored glazes are made by adding various coloring compounds, mainly oxides, to the glaze mix. Cobalt oxide, for instance, is used to give various shades of blue; chromium oxide and copper salts are among the compounds used for green or green-blue shades; lead oxide and antimony oxide with traces of certain other oxides give shades of yellow, and so does titanium mixed with chromium; selenium and cadmium sulfide used together give red; manganese dioxide and iron give browns. However, the ceramist can rely on no simple rule such as x gives yellow, y gives red, z gives blue. The color obtained depends not only on the coloring oxides used but also on the composition of the base glaze into which they are put, the firing temperature, and the atmosphere in the glost kiln. Chromium, for example, which normally gives green or green-blue, will produce a delicate pink when combined with tin oxide in an opaque glaze; copper oxide, which gives dark greens and blues when fired in an oxidizing atmosphere, can—under suitable conditions in a reducing atmosphere—produce the extremely brilliant red of rouge flambé illustrated on page 88.

Close control of color and color-matching (say between a bath and wall tiles for a bathroom) is at once important and difficult. Until recent years it was done subjectively, by eye. Today it is increasingly done with the help of sensitive color-measuring apparatus.

The wall-tile industry, especially, employs a wide range of glaze effects that are often based on the use of mat or semimat glazes. Such glazes, frequently applied far more thickly than transparent glazes, contain substances that crystallize out as the glaze is cooling. They therefore contain crystalline phases, unlike transparent glazes and other transparent glasses, which are wholly amorphous supercooled liquids. Many of these mat or semimat effects rely on the use of titanium dioxide, often in the form of rutile, a natural crystalline form.

For insulator porcelain, as we shall see in Chapter 4, it is sometimes necessary to use glazes that will conduct electricity to a limited extent. Similar ones can also be applied to tiles for use in places where highly inflammable materials are handled, and where sparks produced by the discharge of static electricity could cause an explosion.

Preparation of Glazes

Whatever glaze recipe the ceramist uses he must ensure that all the ingredients are brought to a fine powdery state. If the particles are too fine, however, the glaze will *crawl*, which means that instead of spreading evenly over the surface of the article during firing, it will move rather like water on a greasy surface, covering some areas but leaving others uncovered. If, on the other hand, the particles are too coarse, it will be difficult to keep them suspended in water in the glaze slip. Particle size will also affect

Manual dipping in liquid glaze is a skilled operation, as care must be taken to avoid unevenness and to prevent air bubbles forming between ware and glaze. Large plates are held, as here, with thumb and finger extensions and maneuvered with a skilled turn of the wrist.

Spraying is the most suitable method of applying glaze to heavy ware, as it is quick, but also allows close control of glaze thickness. Small articles are usually sprayed on a conveyor belt, large ones on a turntable as here.

how the glaze matures, glazes composed of coarse particles maturing less readily than those composed of finer ones.

While frits are sometimes ground separately, it is a common practice to mix all the ingredients together and wet-grind them to the required particle size in much the same way as feldspar is ground for the body (Chapter 2). But since, in the case of a glaze mix, it is particularly important to avoid contamination and specking, the grinding cylinder is usually lined not with porcelain or quartz but with rubber. The grinding balls may be of quartz, but nowadays they are very often of alumina, which gives much higher grinding speeds. After grinding, the mixture must be purified by means of a magnet and sieved.

All the main glaze ingredients are hard materials with no plasticity, and the particles when ground are much bigger and heavier than clay particles, being as much as 10 microns in diameter, compared with as little as one tenth of a micron for clay. This means that they will tend to settle out and segregate in the slip.

It is therefore usual to add a few per cent of clay, putting it into the grinding cylinder with the other ingredients. Not only does the clay help in holding the other particles in suspension, but it also improves the application characteristics of the slip.

The proportion of water added to the ingredients, as well as the fluidity and thixotropy of the glaze slip, must be carefully controlled. The exact value required for each of these things depends on how the glaze is to be put on and the nature of the ceramic body to which it is to be applied.

Applying Glazes

The traditional method of applying a glaze to almost all articles was, as we have seen, by dipping them in the glaze slip. In the past two or three decades spraying has come into wider and wider use, first for heavy things such as closets and washbasins, more recently (and now quite frequently) also for tableware.

Manual dipping is a skilled operation. The man who does it must know just how to avoid trapping air between the article and the slip, which is not as easy as it sounds when the article happens to be, say, a jug or a teapot. His fingers must never touch any extensive surface, but only sharp edges and rims, over which the glaze will run during firing, and this means that for biggish tableware, such as dinner plates 25 cm. in diameter, he may need to have a small hook attached to one or more fingers. Perhaps most important, he must acquire the knack of flicking off all excess glaze slip with a few deft movements of the wrist. Some years ago, when sanitary ware was still dipped, the job could be heavy and tiring, and there were other tricks of the trade to be learned. It is difficult to imagine, for instance, how the slip could satisfactorily reach and cover all parts of a closet in one brief dipping. It was a common practice, therefore, to pour a jugful of slip through the trap before immersing the whole closet in the glaze.

Porous biscuit (*biscuit* is the term used to describe unglazed ware after its first firing) raised, and still raises, its own characteristic problems, since the degree of porosity, and therefore the amount of water likely to be absorbed from the slip, varies. A man dipping such ware sometimes uses two tubs, one containing a more watery slip than the other. More porous ware he dips into the more watery slip. In the days when much sanitary ware was made of earthenware, it was often so porous when biscuit-fired that it had to be dipped first into water to prevent it from absorbing too much glaze slip.

Modern sanitary ware, bone china, and other vitreous ware have virtually no porosity. Glaze slips applied to them must therefore be more thixotropic than those applied to porous ware, so that the glaze will thicken up quickly and have enough rigidity to stay in position while water is evaporating from the slip. The glaze at this stage is a feeble layer of noncoherent particles. So that the ware can be handled when the glaze has dried, the ceramist adds some organic binder and hardener, such as sodium carboxy-methyl-cellulose, that will burn out in the glost before the glaze begins to fuse.

Manual dipping, though by no means eliminated, is less common now than formerly, having been largely replaced by devices that carry certain types of ware mechanically through a bath of slip. Incidentally, there is no longer the same need to judge differences in porosity of earthenware biscuit as there used to be, since firing in tunnel kilns results in greater uniformity of porosity than did firing in old-style intermittents.

Wall tiles, which are glazed on one side only, call for modifications in dipping techniques. Today they are commonly conveyed mechanically, on two parallel strings, through a waterfall of glaze slip, which covers only their upper surface and edges; little mechanical fingers clear the slip from the edges as they move on. They then pass under radiant-heat driers, which very rapidly dry the glaze so that the tiles can be removed from the conveyor. With the waterfall technique, as with any dipping technique, the slip must be constantly agitated to prevent the differential settling of particles of various weight and size.

In Europe, some very heavy sanitary ware—such as urinals and large kitchen sinks for schools, hospitals, and so on—is still made from fireclay bodies. These bodies are of a dark color, and a common practice is to cover such articles after firing first with a white *engobe* (a clay-based ceramic mixture) and then with a white opaque glaze. Since the articles are so big and heavy as to make dipping difficult, both engobe and glaze are often applied

"Waterfalling" of wall tiles. Tiles to be glazed on one side only are conveyed mechanically, on two parallel wires, through a waterfall of glaze slip that covers only their upper surfaces and edges. Surplus slip is cleared from the edges of the tiles as they pass on.

by brushing. For this purpose gelatine is added to form a highly thixotropic mixture of blancmange-like consistency.

Today, however, almost all products of this kind, and almost all other large ceramic articles, are glazed by spraying, in much the same way as car bodies are paint-sprayed. This method lends itself to far better control of the thickness of the glaze coating, since several coats can be added if necessary and the thickness can be varied from point to point.

Spraying can be either semimechanized or wholly mechanized. Where it is semimechanized the articles move along on a conveyor, passing through one or more glazing stations where a man directs a spray of glaze onto them. In each glazing booth, air-extraction plant prevents dried glaze particles from filling the atmosphere. Spray that misses the articles goes onto a wall at the back of the booth that is continuously "waterfalled"; the waste glaze is then pumped back, the water extracted from it, and the glaze material salvaged. Where spraying is wholly mechanized (mainly for smaller articles) the ware passes through a short tunnel in which sprays of glaze are directed continuously onto it.

The thickness of glaze applied diminishes by roughly half during firing, due mainly to the elimination of spaces between the particles of the unfired glaze. On most tableware the fired thickness is about one hundredth of a centimeter, and on most sanitary ware a little thicker, while on colored and decorated wall tiles, artware, and some kinds of tableware the glaze may be far thicker. Control of thickness is important because it affects the rate at which the glaze matures, and the modern trend is to glost-fire faster and faster. With colored and opaque glazes changes of thickness will also result in variations of color. The thinner the glaze layer the more pronounced will be the effects of the body color on what one actually sees; further, too thin a layer of glaze will not contain sufficient particles of pigment to give the strength of color required.

The techniques used for glazing unfired ware (that is, ware that undergoes only a single firing) are basically the same as those for fired ware, except that articles which are dried but unfired need more careful handling. Since unfired bodies are more porous, and usually of a finer texture, than fired ones, however, the fluid properties of the glaze slip need to be somewhat different.

Some parts of certain ceramic articles must not be glazed at all. An instance is the end of a trap which must later be fitted into the rest of a closet. Such parts are covered, perhaps with a rubber band or a coating of liquid wax, before dipping or spraying.

Glost Firing

Wares that were biscuit-fired before the glaze was applied must next be glost-fired. This is now usually done in tunnel kilns or in modern intermittents that either use some clean-burning fuel or are equipped with a muffle, since it is essential that the ware does not come into contact with sulfurous gases, which would ruin the glaze surface and might even cause crystals to form on it. (In old coal-burning intermittent kilns glazed wares must be protected from the inevitable sulfurous atmosphere by setting them in saggers.) Tunnel kilns employed for glost firing are generally shorter and of smaller cross section than those that

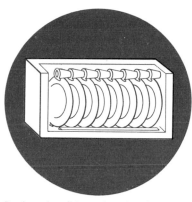

During glost firing, glazed surfaces must not touch or they would stick together as the glaze melted. Articles such as plates are therefore kept apart by using refractory supports, as shown above. Below: a loaded truck entering the kiln for glost firing.

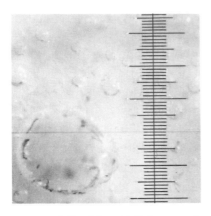

Air-filled spaces between particles of glaze form minute bubbles when the glaze reaches fusing temperature. Left: photomicrograph (x 25) showing how, on cooling, the thin upper skin of bubbles is sucked in to form unsightly craters. Right: photomicrographs (all x 25) show how bubbles are eliminated by increasing the period for which ware is kept at maximum glost firing temperature. From left to right: 0 hours, 4 hours, 10 hours, and 70 hours.

are used for biscuit firing, and operate at temperatures 100°c or more below those of the corresponding biscuit kiln; they also fire much faster. Tableware, for instance, may go through the glost kiln in seven or eight hours, and the firing temperature will probably be in the region of 1050°c.

Setting for glost firing is broadly similar to that for biscuit firing, except that glazed surfaces must not touch, otherwise they would stick together as the glaze melted. Articles that have an unglazed surface (such as the foot of a china plate, which can be ground and polished), will therefore stand on that surface. Flatware that is glazed all over (as is that of earthenware) can be set either in vertical racks, each plate or saucer being supported on three tiny pins, or in horizontal racks, each article being supported between *saddles* (below) and *thimbles* (above), as shown in the diagram on page 101. Dishes are often supported rim downward on small bowl pins, while cups and vases commonly rest bottom downward on the tips of Y-shaped *stilts*. Thimbles, saddles, and stilts are made of fireclay and so designed that the weight rests only on sharp points, which leave no more than tiny marks on the glaze. These marks can subsequently be effaced by careful grinding.

It was mentioned in Chapter 2 that European porcelain tableware becomes fully vitrified only during its second firing—that is, after the glaze is applied. Unlike other tableware, it is therefore liable to distortion and shrinkage during glost firing. Precautions

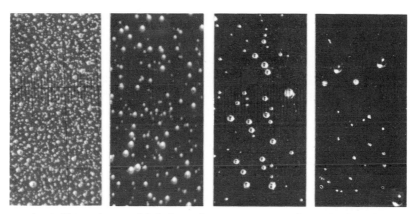

against distortion, which in other cases are taken during firing, are here taken during glost firing. Cups, for instance, are sometimes boxed, as described on page 85. However, since cups glazed all over would stick together if boxed for glost firing, the rims of European porcelain cups that are to be boxed are left unglazed, and later ground and polished.

Before wares go to the glost kiln, about half the total volume of the powdery glaze layer on their surface consists of irregularly shaped air-filled spaces between the particles of glaze material. When the glaze reaches the temperature at which it starts to fuse, these air-filled spaces get sealed over and form tens of thousands of minute bubbles that, if left in, would reduce the brightness of the finished glaze. As the temperature increases, these minute bubbles join together to form larger ones, sufficiently large to impair perceptibly the smoothness of the glaze surface. In addition, pressure inside bubbles nearest the surface may decrease during cooling, sucking in the thin upper skin and forming craters. The elimination of bubbles is therefore important, and depends to some extent on the rate at which the temperature is raised to the maximum, the length of time it is held there, and the rate at which cooling takes place. Close control of the entire firing curve (see Chapter 1) is therefore important if a smooth and attractive glaze is to be obtained.

The *fit* of a glaze depends on its own thermal expansion and that of the body it covers. The thermal expansion of a ceramic body is determined partly by its chemical composition and such physical factors as particle size, and partly by its firing treatment. That of the glaze is determined almost entirely by its composition. As the glaze, after reaching maturing temperature, begins to cool, it will become more and more viscous and eventually rigid. From then on down to room temperature both glaze and body will go on contracting, and the glaze must, of course, shrink to the same final extent as the body to which it is then rigidly attached. If the glaze has a lower thermal expansion than the body, its tendency will be to shrink less in cooling; but because it must in fact shrink just as much, it will be under compression. Glazes under compression are very strong, and actually add to the strength of the body. If the glaze has a higher thermal expansion than the body, its tendency will be to shrink more in cooling; but because it must in fact shrink only as·much, it will be under tension. Glazes under tension are weak, and very likely to *craze* (show a network of cracks). The ceramist therefore aims at achieving a glaze that is under compression; but it must not be excessively so, otherwise it will tend to peel or flake off.

The "fit" of a glaze depends on its thermal expansion being less than that of the body it covers. If its thermal expansion is sufficiently less than that of the body, it will shrink less than the body during cooling, and will therefore be in a state of compression when cold. Insufficient compression results in the crazing effect shown here.

On porous ware even a glaze that is initially under compression may craze after the ware has been in use for some time. This is because almost all porous ceramic bodies actually grow in size, and grow permanently, by adsorbing water, the rate of growth under constant condition of exposure being comparatively great at first and less later. As the porous body continues to grow, the glaze covering it is under decreasing compression and may eventually be under tension, and at that state it may craze. With all glazed porous ware the ceramist first ensures that the initial compression of the glaze is on the high side, and then employs delayed-crazing tests, such as exposing the articles to steam at a pressure of around 3.5 kg/cm^2 for many hours before putting them on the market. Often, too, the moisture expansion of the body itself is reduced by including a few per cent of magnesia, lime, or calcium carbonate in it, all of which help in the production of a glassy bond with a lower moisture expansion.

If a glaze with a lower thermal expansion than the body were applied to a perfectly flat wall tile, the difference in stresses between the glazed and unglazed sides would pull the tile out of shape, leaving it slightly convex on the glazed side. It is to compensate for this that wall tiles are rendered slightly concave during biscuit firing, as described in Chapter 2, and the glaze later applied to the concave surface.

Salt glazing, still often used for stoneware pipes fired in open-flame continuous chamber kilns or old-type intermittents, is unique among glazing processes. When the pipes are within about 100°c of their firing temperature (anything between 1150°c and 1250°c) a small quantity of moist common salt, frequently mixed with a small proportion of borax, is introduced into the kiln, where it volatilizes. The chlorine from the salt combines with water vapor to form hydrochloric acid fumes, which escape from the kiln chimney; the sodium reacts with the silica and alumina in the clay at the surface of the pipes and forms a sodium aluminosilicate glaze. We saw in Chapter 2 that this process is now on the decline because more and more pipes are being fired in tunnel kilns, in which salt glazing is extremely difficult. Another factor is that while an orthodox ceramic glaze increases the strength of a pipe, for reasons we have seen, salt glazing reduces it.

Decorating

For decorating pottery the ceramist relies on a wide range of coloring compounds (mainly metal oxides) mixed with other ingredients that enable them to fuse with the glaze. Ceramic colors can be applied either before glazing (underglaze decoration) or after (overglaze decoration). Underglaze decoration has the advantage of being completely protected from wear by the glaze, but the disadvantage of limiting the range of colors that can be used. This is because underglaze colors must be subjected to the full maturing temperature of the glaze, and at increasingly high temperatures increasing numbers of coloring compounds will burn out, react with the glaze, or even dissolve in it. The range of underglaze colors available is therefore narrowest with the feldspathic glazes, maturing at 1400° to 1450°c, used for European porcelain, and widest with the fritted glazes, maturing at 1020° to 1080°c, used for earthenware, other china tableware, and wall tiles.

When overglaze colors are applied, the already glazed ware has only to undergo a subsequent firing, called enamel firing, at a much lower temperature, commonly in the region of 750° to 800°c. This is usually done in short electrically fired tunnel kilns of very small cross-section and takes only a few hours. Overglaze decoration greatly extends the ceramist's palette. At the same time, while durable enough for all practical purposes, it is less well protected from wear than underglaze decoration.

The comparatively recent advent of detergent and dishwashing machines at first increased the wear and tear on overglaze colors, but intensive research work has resulted not only in the production of colors with greatly increased resistance to abrasion and to attack by alkalis, but also in detergents that, though retaining their cleansing powers, are less severe on ceramic colors.

Coloring compounds used for underglaze decoration are calcined with a substance such as feldspar or china clay, and the mixture ground to a very fine powder. Those used for overglaze decoration are mixed and ground with frits containing a high proportion of soft fluxes such as lead, soda, and potash, since they must soften at considerably lower temperatures. To make printing oils for underglaze decoration the ingredients can be mixed with linseed oil thickened by heating, and with smaller quantities of additives such as Stockholm tar, gum, and resin. The usual medium for underglaze and overglaze painting is a mixture of turpentine and fat oil, or their equivalents based on processed or synthetic resins.

When underglaze decoration is applied to ware, it may add an extra link to the chain of production processes. This is because where biscuit ware carries a pattern formed by an oily ink it will repel the watery glaze slip, while elsewhere it will not. Hence if the glaze slip is applied without further processing, the resultant layer of glaze material may not be evenly enough distributed. For this reason biscuit ware carrying underglaze decoration sometimes has to undergo a preliminary firing at a temperature of about 600°c to burn out all organic substances. This is called hardening-on. Overglaze decoration, of course, never calls for this process. Where a number of overglaze colors are used on one article, however, some may have a different maturing temperature from others. It may therefore be necessary to fire some colors, then apply others and fire again; and for highly decorated ware the process may have to be repeated several times.

Color decoration can be applied in many ways, ranging from hand painting to printing. Successful hand painting calls for considerable skill and judgment, since the colors used will generally change during firing, and the man who applies them must consider how they will blend after they have been through the enameling kiln, rather than how they blend raw. Hand painting is therefore a slow and expensive process confined mainly to the decoration of high-quality artware. Various other methods, including stenciling, and stamping on designs with the aid of a rubber stamp and a pad impregnated with ceramic ink, are too time-consuming to find more than an occasional place in large-scale production.

The most widely used mass-production method of applying a colored pattern is by means of paper transfers. These are usually printed from lithographic plates in much the same way as other printed matter but using varnish instead of normal printing inks; ceramic colors in powder form are then dusted on and adhere only where there is varnish on the paper. Such transfers are

The groundlaying process. When a colored background (groundlay) is required to contrast with a painted or printed design, those areas not to receive this (i.e. those that are to be patterned) are first stenciled with a water-soluble medium. The plates in the foreground have been stenciled in this way, while the groundlayer is seen applying the background color. The water-soluble resist is washed off before the plates are fired.

Applying transfers to tableware. Transfers for printing ceramics are made from lithographic plates using varnish instead of inks. Ceramic colors in powder form are then dusted on and adhere to the varnished areas.

Many printed patterns are enriched by ceramic colors best applied by hand painting, seen here. This is a highly skilled process. Since colors used will change during firing, the artist must take into account how they will blend after firing rather than how they blend raw.

Applying finely ground gold, mixed with resins, to glazed tableware. During enamel firing, the resins burn out, leaving a thin layer of the pure metal attached to the glazed surface.

Simple designs can be printed by this automatic offset machine. An engraved copper plate is inked and the imprint taken off onto a parabola-shaped gelatin pad. This is then lowered (right) onto the article to print the design.

known in Britain as *lithos*, and in America as *decalcomania*, or *decals*. They are commonly wetted and then pressed or rubbed onto the ware by hand with a roller, the paper later being peeled off. Transfers can also be produced by intaglio printing—that is, from engraved printing plates.

Particularly where high density of color is required, the ceramist may make use of silk-screen printing, employing it either directly or with the aid of transfers. He can also use a device in which a flexible pad is pressed first onto an engraved printing plate and then onto the wares.

Both gold and platinum play a very important part in the decoration of tableware. When finely ground and combined with resins they can be applied either by the overglaze techniques just described, or in the case of lines and bends, simply with a brush. During enamel firing the resins burn out, leaving a thin layer of pure metal attached to the glazed surface. This metallic layer can be etched or burnished to produce the various aesthetic effects required. In many modern factories gold and platinum decorations are applied as solutions of organic compounds of these metals, which give a bright surface after firing and do not require any further treatment. Semiautomatic machines are often used to apply these liquid metal preparations.

However much care the potter takes at every stage of production, he knows that the appeal of his tableware will depend very largely on its design. A first-class design team is therefore one of his greatest assets, and being a wise man he usually treats it accordingly.

4 Ceramics and Electricity

Some two and a half centuries of experiment with frictional machines and static electricity, from the mid-16th century onward, produced only one marketable invention: Benjamin Franklin's lightning conductor. The three decades following Volta's discovery that an electric current could be produced by chemical means, in a "pile" or battery, added little new to industry except electroplating, but they did give scientists time to study the magnetic effects of an electric current. Faraday's discovery of electromagnetic induction in 1831, which ultimately made it possible to produce far larger currents continuously and at lower cost, soon had a variety of uses. In Britain the railway age was already in its lusty infancy, and by 1840 the electric telegraph solved the problems of sending signals faster than a train could travel. Over the next few years the telegraph was installed wherever new railways were built. Then in the 1870s and 1880s came two further inventions destined to spread with equal rapidity: the telephone and the electric filament lamp.

All ceramic insulators must be rigorously tested before use. Here an impulse test, which simulates the effects of lightning, is being carried out on a 400 KV post insulator.

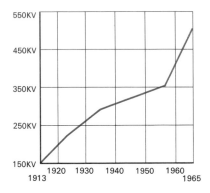

Maximum transmission voltages have risen steeply during this century in most industrialized European countries and in the United States (shown here). It is an increase that has made increasingly stringent demands upon insulator equipment.

All these called for the large-scale production not only of conductors but also of insulators. An electrical conductor can be defined as a material in which electrons can move easily from one atom to another, thus carrying a current when even a small potential difference is applied. An electrical insulator can be defined as a material in which electrons and ions are far more tightly bound together, and that will therefore carry a current only when a much larger potential difference is applied. All the mid-19th century uses of electric power required only fairly low voltages, and made no great demands on the electrical and mechanical properties of insulators. For telegraph or telephone insulators, as for domestic switch-bases, fuse-holders, bulb sockets, and so on, almost any kind of insulating material will work provided it can resist the flow of a current with a pressure of at most a few hundred volts and provided it is durable. Ceramic materials, first stoneware and later porcelain, were for many years the main ones employed for such purposes, largely because they are inexpensive, easy to clean, and comparatively easy to manufacture in complicated shapes. Various plastics with similar advantages later captured a considerable share of the market. By 1900 the use of three-phase AC current had begun, which meant that transformers could be used to increase voltages. As demand, power outputs, and—with the development of grid systems—transmission distances, all increased, voltages increased with them. While the highest transmission voltages of 50 years ago were very much below 100 KV, they have now reached 500 KV, and voltages half as great again are in prospect by 1970. Voltages are increasing at the same rate in every industrial country. Without high-quality, and often very large, insulators for transformer switch-gear and for high-voltage overhead cables, the whole system of power distribution on which modern industry depends would come to a standstill. So would the many electrified railways that now operate at voltages of up to 25 KV. Yet no material combines in the highest degree all the electrical and mechanical properties that are desirable for ideal high-voltage insulation; each has to make the best of what properties it has.

Electrical Properties

The electrical properties that matter most are high volume and surface resistivity, high puncture strength, and good tracking resistance.

Resistivity is simply the resistance that a material offers to the passage of a current. *Volume resistivity* is the resistance that a cube of material measuring $1 \times 1 \times 1$ cm. offers to the passage of a current through it when a voltage difference is applied to two of its opposite faces, and is expressed in ohms multiplied by centimeters. At room temperature (say 20°C) insulator porcelain has a volume resistivity of about 10^{14} ohm-cm, which is several thousand times as great as that of celluloid and between ten and a hundred times as great as that of rubber, or of common glass containing soda. However, insulating materials behave in the opposite way to conducting materials in that their resistivity decreases as their temperature rises, and in the case of porcelain a rise in temperature from 20° to 200°C reduces the volume resistivity 10,000-fold. The resistivity of any insulator must therefore be sufficient to meet the demands made on it at the highest temperature to which it will be exposed in service.

High volume resistivity is of little use if current can flow over the surface of an insulator from one side to the other. Surface resistivity must also be adequate. In fact, that of unglazed porcelain is good enough for all practical purposes, provided the atmosphere is dry; but in a very humid atmosphere unglazed

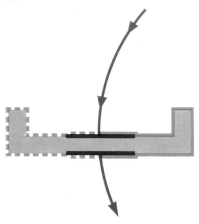

Method of testing the puncture or dielectric strength of an insulator. Voltage difference (red) is applied in such a way that the surface route (blue) is too great for flashover to occur. When the voltage difference is sufficiently great, the temperature of the insulator rises and its resistivity falls until it conducts the current, at which point it will become punctured.

porcelain with a fairly rough surface will collect a film of water and dirt, which may cut down its surface resistivity in dry conditions, and which increases it by about a hundredfold at very high humidities. For this reason ceramic insulators are glazed to provide a suitably smooth surface; water-repellent silicone finishes have a similar effect, though they are less permanent than a glaze.

We have seen that volume resistivity is measured by applying a potential difference to opposite surfaces of a piece of insulating material. If the voltage is steadily raised, and if at the same time the surface route between the two opposite surfaces is too great for the charge to traverse by flashing over (as in the testing method shown on page 129), then the temperature of the insulator will rise with a consequent fall in resistivity. Sooner or later there will be an avalanche of charged ions inside it sufficient to conduct a current through it, and with the passage of the current the insulator will puncture. The higher the voltage needed to puncture it, the better is the insulator. In fact the *puncture strength* (dielectric strength) of any given insulating material, usually measured in kilovolts per millimeter, varies with the thickness of the sample, the temperature at which the test is carried out, the rate at which the voltage is increased, and whether the current is AC or DC. Puncture strength decreases with increased thickness and increased temperature, and increases with an increase in the rate of raising the voltage; in addition, puncture strength is generally lower for AC at normal power frequencies than for DC. The more microflaws (cracks and pores) there are in an insulator the more easily it will puncture under electric stress. Although porcelain has virtually no apparent porosity (that is, porosity of the kind that gives rise to permeability), it commonly has a true porosity (due to closed internal pores) of about five per cent. These pores, coupled with minute internal cracks, make it possible for charged ions to carry a current over a comparatively easy point-to-point route through it. Glass insulators, which are free from such microflaws, therefore have a much higher puncture strength than porcelain insulators. Thus puncture-strength tests, though of little importance with glass, are of the utmost importance with porcelain.

When flashover occurs, the surfaces of some insulating materials, such as plastics, tend to burn, leaving tracks of carbon, which then serve as conductors. Both porcelain and glass insulators are completely track-proof, even if flashover heats and temporarily melts their surfaces.

Another property that makes both porcelain and glass particularly suitable for high-voltage insulators is their weather-resistance. An insulator for a high-voltage transmission line can be expected to stay in service out-of-doors continuously for as long as 20 years, whether in the Arctic, with frequent blizzards and temperatures as low as $-40°c$, or in tropical deserts, where it will encounter sandstorms and where its temperature in the sun may rise as high as 60° to 80°c. Only extremely hard and chemically inert inorganic materials like porcelain and glass can stand up to such conditions without showing signs of severe wear and tear.

Mechanical Properties

On balance, the electrical properties that matter most in high-voltage insulators are better combined in porcelain than in any other material with the possible exception of glass. Some of the mechanical properties of porcelain, however, are very different from those of the iron and steel with which it is combined in insulator manufacture, and this poses problems that must be solved by careful design and special manufacturing techniques.

For instance, the tensile strength of ordinary, plastically shaped, glazed porcelain (i.e. the pull it can withstand without breaking) is about 560 kg/cm^2, compared with up to 4200 kg/cm^2 for malleable cast iron. On the other hand the compressive strength of ordinary glazed porcelain is surprisingly high—as great as that of some metals. The ceramist can, in fact, increase the tensile strength of insulator porcelain far beyond that of ordinary porcelain by increasing the alumina content of the body. More importantly, wherever possible he arranges the design of complex insulators in such a way that the material is stressed in compression rather than in tension. The diagram on page 119 shows how this can be done.

Porcelain is strictly elastic, which means that it will stretch or bend to an extent directly proportional to the force acting on it at any given moment, and when that force is removed it will instantaneously go back to its former dimensions. Metals, however, exhibit a phenomenon called *yield*, which means that when they stretch or bend due to the application of a powerful force, they do not always recover their original dimensions when that force is removed; they may show a slight permanent set. The harder it is to stretch a material, the higher is its Young's modulus. That of porcelain is about 840,000 kg/cm^2, compared with 1½ to 2 million kg/cm^2 for iron and steel. Another notable difference between porcelain and metals is that porcelain will stretch by only 0.05 per cent without breaking, while iron and steel will stretch considerably more. Again, iron and steel have a higher thermal expansion than porcelain. All these differences pose difficult design problems when iron or steel is combined with porcelain in an insulator.

The impact strength of all ceramic materials, including porcelain (that is, their ability to withstand blows without cracking), is rather low, but it depends to a large extent on the shape of the article. Thin sharp edges will render it weaker, and thicker gentler curving ones will render it stronger. So here again design can have a marked effect on performance.

Like most materials that are good electrical insulators, porcelain is also a good thermal insulator. This, coupled with the fact that it has lower tensile strength and higher specific heat than metals

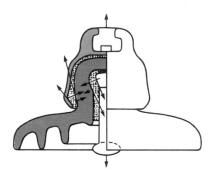

Cross section of a disk insulator unit. The mechanical strength of porcelain, like most ceramic materials, is greater in compression than in tension. For this reason disk insulator units, which are in tension during service, must be designed to ensure that the main stresses on the porcelain component are of a compressive nature. This diagram shows how metal (gray), porcelain (red), and jointing cement (speckled area) are used to achieve this.

with which it is combined, means that special steps must be taken in design to ensure that the finished insulator will withstand the fairly severe thermal shocks that it will meet in service. These include the hazard of being struck by lightning, and exposure to storms of rain or hail following spells of hot sunshine.

Insulator Manufacture

Every stage of insulator manufacture contributes to exploiting the electrical and mechanical properties of porcelain to full advantage. The body preparation is much the same as for domestic porcelain and china, and the main ingredients are still clay, feldspar, and quartz. However, the ingredients are not all used in quite the same proportions. Since whiteness is of no great importance, the proportion of china clays can be reduced and that of more plastic clays increased. This produces a body that is more workable while in the plastic state and mechanically stronger in the dry state. Among other modifications, as we have seen, alumina may also be added to the body when necessary to increase tensile strength.

A typical composition for insulator porcelain would be:

	percentage by weight
Blended plastic ball clays	30
Blended china clays	17
Ground quartz	25
Potash feldspar	28

It has been emphasized that careful internal design is essential to allow for the mechanical differences between the porcelain and metal parts of an insulator. Without proper external design, a high-voltage insulator simply would not fulfil its function at all; and because designs are necessarily complicated, the potter's traditional shaping methods often have to be modified. Most of the methods described in Chapter 2 are in fact used, but extrusion and lathe-turning play a far bigger part here than in the manufacture of domestic wares, and there is often a good deal of machining and assembly to be done after firing.

The higher the voltage, the greater the distance it will jump through air, and at very high voltages the distance may be several meters. This at once raises questions of sheer size, because the total length of the insulator must obviously be greater than the possible jumping distance. But a current can also flow over the surface of an insulator, since there will inevitably be some surface conductivity. Therefore, the path along the surface must always be a very long one, and projecting ridges ("sheds") are introduced into the design to make it so. For insulators that are to serve in regions subject to high humidities and atmospheric pollution, even longer creepage paths are needed. This is achieved by introducing a series of deep anti-fog sheds or "petticoats." Drip-rings may also have to be provided to ensure that water runs off the insulator.

Sheer size coupled with complexity of design means that very

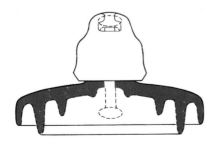

Design of insulator units. To prevent leakage current flowing over the surface of the insulator, the path along the surface must be a long one. For insulators that are to serve in areas of heavy pollution, especially long surface (or creepage) paths are needed. This unit has a diameter of 381 mm. and a total creepage path (due to the projecting anti-fog sheds or "petticoats") of 578 mm.

Jollying a large insulator unit. Great care must be taken to avoid air pockets, which would be fatal to the functioning of the insulator.

Large, complex insulators may be made up of several individually jollied sections that are stuck together, as shown here, with a slip of similar composition to the body.

high-voltage insulators can seldom be shaped in one piece. A typical example is provided by suspension insulators for grid lines. In many countries, including Britain and the United States, these consist of strings of disk insulators. Each disk is made either by jollying or by warm plastic pressing.

Although jollying here is basically the same as for cups and plates, it calls for more skill. This is because the articles concerned are far bigger, thicker, and heavier, which means that air pockets, which would be fatal to the functioning of an insulator, could form more easily during shaping. The operative also has to work to fine dimensional limits. For these reasons the jollying process for insulators is seldom if ever completely mechanized, and the jollying of a single disk may take minutes, as compared with seconds for an automatically jollied plate. Jollying is usually followed by some surface finishing and fettling, done by hand after the disk is partially dried and removed from the mold.

The alternative method of shaping such insulators is to press the plastic body between warm dies, which give both the internal and external shape. This process lends itself more readily to mechanization, but it sometimes calls for modification in insulator design, as it is difficult to form reentrant shapes between two dies.

Post, or pedestal, insulators, used as supports for high-voltage busbars in substations and high-voltage switch-gear, often consist of a number of units that are bolted together after firing. The units themselves are commonly so complex in shape that each one must be made up of two or three sections that are jollied individually, dried, and fired, then cemented together. High-voltage bushings and weathersheds may be three meters or more in height, about one meter in diameter, and weigh about 1000 kg. They consist of perhaps a score of huge rings, each with one or more sheds. All the rings are shaped by jollying, and when partially dried they are stuck together with a slip of similar composition to the body, in much the same way as the separate pieces of a closet. The slip is applied in a thin layer, and the finished joint must be free from microscopic flaws and homogeneous with the rest of the insulator, otherwise the whole bushing might fail electrically after firing.

Jollying, though widely used in insulator manufacture, is a somewhat slow process. However, there are many small and medium-size articles, such as pin insulators and small post insulators, that can be shaped much faster by semimechanized lathe-turning. For such articles the plastic body is extruded from a de-airing pug mill, and cut into the lengths needed. To form any necessary grooves or sheds, each such blank, after partial drying to render it leather-hard, is turned on a semiautomatic lathe where the cutting tools are guided by accurate profile plates. Most insulators are turned on horizontal lathes, but in fairly recent years the introduction of vertical lathes has made it possible to extend this process to much bigger insulators.

It is sometimes convenient to fashion the porcelain parts of insulators by slip casting, using the same techniques as those employed in the production of vitreous china sanitary ware, but the method is not a very common one. Dust-pressing, the process used for shaping wall tiles, plays a considerable part in the production of small insulators such as switch-bases and fuse-holders, though in this case the dust must be coarser and wetter, because of the far more complicated shapes involved. However, the properties of dust-pressed porcelain are such that it can be used only for low-tension work.

Because of their thickness, all high-voltage insulators must be dried slowly. At the time of shaping, a bushing weighing about 500 kg. contains some 113 liters of water, which must be driven out as several thousand cubic meters of vapor before firing. Such large insulators are dried in individual chambers that enable rigorous control of temperature and humidity to be exercised throughout the process.

Insulators are fired only once, and the glazes used are therefore almost invariably high-temperature nonfritted feldspathic glazes, applied by either dipping or spraying. The most commonly used glaze color is brown, produced by adding small quantities of iron and manganese oxides, though some customers specify white or green glazes. As for all once-fired ceramic articles, the glaze must contain binders and adhesives to keep it firm after the water has evaporated from the glaze slip, in order to prevent damage between glaze application and firing.

In some cases, all or part of an insulator is covered with a semi-conducting glaze, to give surface resistivity very much lower than that of porcelain, but very much higher than that of any common metal, usually in the region of 20 million ohms (megohms). Such glazes are produced by including either ferrites or a pro-portion of certain metallic oxides, such as tin oxide or antimony oxide, in the glaze mix. They are used on that part of an insulator that will be in direct contact with a cable where there would otherwise be a risk of interference with radio and television, due to sparking. By coating the entire porcelain surface of a complex insulator with a semiconducting glaze, a much more uniform distribution of potential is obtained, as a result of the small leakage current that flows over it to earth. This enables the insulator to be operated at higher ratings than would otherwise be possible.

Nowadays all small and medium-size insulators are fired in tunnel kilns. In Britain and America this is done in an oxidizing

Left: turning a large insulator unit by hand on a semimechanized vertical lathe. The cutting tool is guided by an accurately cut profile to ensure uniform dimensions.

Below: removing a carload of large porcelain insulators from a modern automatic intermittent kiln.

atmosphere at temperatures not usually much above 1200°c, but in continental Europe ceramists often follow the traditional porcelain practice of firing in a reducing atmosphere at temperatures of around 1400°c. Because of their size and thickness, porcelain insulators must be fired slowly, and the time through the kiln may be up to 50 or 60 hours, as compared with something between 15 and 25 hours for most sanitary ware. Very large insulators, including some that are assembled into one piece before firing, usually go into special intermittent kilns fired by gas, oil, or electricity, and elaborate precautions, including the use of refractory props, are taken to prevent them from distorting under their own weight. The tallest insulators are not infrequently fired in top-hat kilns that will just fit over one, or maybe two, of them. Due to firing shrinkage, these very tall insulators may emerge from the kiln something between 30 and 70 cm. shorter than they entered it. Such insulators are fired more slowly than those fired in a tunnel kiln.

Pre-Assembly Testing

The fired porcelain is but one component of a finished insulator. Before it goes on for assembly with the metal components it must undergo electrical and dimensional tests, and sometimes mechanical tests, though these are mostly done after assembly.

In the pre-assembly routine electrical test, every insulator is submitted to a much higher voltage than it will experience in

Carrying out temperature-cycle tests on insulator units. One tank is refrigerated and the other heated to provide a thermal shock greater than anything the units are likely to encounter during service.

service, to a point just high enough to give flashover. This voltage is usually maintained for several minutes, during which time any faulty insulator will puncture. The insulators usually stand on an earthbed turntable above which is a high-voltage busbar. A number of metal chains, each with one mica link, are suspended from the busbar in such a way that the bottom of each chain touches the bottom internal surface of an insulator. All the time an insulator is functioning properly no current flows, but the moment one punctures a current does flow. The heating effect of the high-voltage current immediately ignites the mica link, and the chain falls into the faulty insulator. Such tests are normally carried out at power frequencies (50 or 60 cycles per second), but more searching tests are sometimes made at frequencies of 100 kilocycles or more. Internal flaws, particularly the presence of air pockets, can also be detected by ultrasonic techniques of the kind used for continuous depthsounding at sea.

Although control techniques have improved enormously in recent years, and are still improving, they have not yet reached the stage where the ceramist can guarantee that products straight from the kiln will fall within the fine dimensional tolerances required for precision engineering purposes, or that unglazed mating surfaces will have the requisite near-perfection. Many of the porcelain components of insulators may therefore need to be ground or turned before going on for assembly. Some of the lathes and grinders are especially designed to take very large insulators, and all of them are equipped with cutting or grinding tools made of alumina, or even of diamond, because of the extreme hardness of porcelain.

Assembly

Insulator assembly consists essentially of joining porcelain to porcelain and porcelain to metal. For both purposes the material most commonly employed is cement, usually Portland cement, but sometimes a high-alumina cement such as *ciment fondu*, which has greater mechanical strength. The cement is used either neat or mixed with some finely powdered inert material, and its water content, thoroughness of mixing, and time of mixing are carefully controlled to give the consistency and setting properties required.

Assembling a large post insulator in a jig. To prevent the formation of voids, which would seriously affect electrical properties, the cement is compacted by vibration while the components are still in the assembly jig.

To ensure good bonding, the porcelain jointing surfaces are sand-glazed. This is done by coating them with a layer of fairly fine, hard grit when the glaze is applied. As the glaze melts during firing, the grit adheres firmly to the porcelain, giving a rough surface that serves as a key for the cement.

The metals used in high-voltage insulators are either malleable cast iron or some special steel, depending on the service to which the insulator will be put. Whatever they are, they must be adequately galvanized before assembly to prevent corrosion. To allow for the difference in expansion between metal and porcelain, the metal is coated with bitumen before cementing. It may also be necessary to insert pads of some resilient material such as cork between the metal and porcelain components.

The parts to be joined are assembled in jigs that hold them accurately in position, and the fairly stiff cement often has to be poured into quite narrow gaps between them. In these conditions voids could result, which would destroy the electrical properties of the insulator as a whole. The cement is therefore vibrated into a compact entity while the components are still in the jig, then left to set sufficiently to allow further handling. The

128

Sand-glazed jointing surface of an insulator unit. Cement is used to join porcelain to porcelain, and porcelain to metal, during assembly. To ensure good jointing, surfaces are given a rough coating of fine hard grit to serve as a key for the cement.

Steam-curing assembled insulator units. The object of this process is to accelerate setting shrinkage of the cement to ensure complete mechanical stability of the assembly.

whole assembly is then removed from the jig and put into a steam-curing cabinet, somewhat like a Turkish bath, for perhaps 24 hours. This accelerates the setting shrinkage of the cement so that the insulator will leave the works in a stable condition. Joints to be exposed to the weather are coated with some weather-proofing compound.

Although cement is commonly regarded as an insulator, its conductivity is considerably greater than that of porcelain. By the use of suitable additives, the insulator manufacturer may actually increase its conductivity and turn this seeming drawback to advantage. When semiconducting glazes are used to equalize the distribution of potential in a complex insulator, as described earlier, the leakage current must be able to flow from one porcelain surface to another; a cement joint with just sufficient conductivity enables it to do this.

Cement is by far the commonest jointing material, but not the only one. Epoxy resins are also sometimes used, and so are glazes. We have seen that large bushings are often made by slip jointing the individual rings before firing. Alternatively, it is possible to glaze the jointing surfaces of the unfired rings, so that in firing the glaze melts and welds them together. Yet another method is to fire the rings separately, then grind the mating surfaces and join them with an epoxy resin adhesive.

No matter what assembly technique is used, it must be such that the finished insulator will fall within very narrow dimensional limits. Furthermore, however good all the porcelain components may be, even one poor joint could ruin the performance of the entire insulator. The importance of sound jointing is emphasized by the fact that the post insulator shown on page 112 contains more than 60 joints between surfaces.

Post-Assembly Testing

The exact nature of this testing depends on the service conditions the insulator will be called on to meet, so that one destined only to support a weight resting on it and to give adequate insulation at 25 KV need not, for instance, be severely tested for tensile strength or submitted to the highest transmission voltages.

Two of the routine post-assembly tests on insulators. Below: vibration test, in which a cantilever load is applied to the top of the insulator while it is under tension. Right: wet flashover test on a pedestal post insulator.

However, in every insulator works there must be equipment available for the routine testing of tensile, torsional, and cantilever strength, as well as ability to withstand vibration and thermal shock. In addition, finished insulators must undergo dry and wet flashover tests and also impulse tests in which they are subjected to sudden increases of voltage. Several testing methods are shown in the photographs on page 129. It has to be remembered that severe mechanical tests may cause microflaws to develop in an insulator (sufficient to impair its electrical qualities) and yet leave it with no visible signs of damage. For this reason, and to save time, a high-voltage power supply is often connected to mechanical testing devices, so that combined electromechanical tests can be made.

Insulators of new design are submitted to extremely elaborate tests (normally specified and observed by the appropriate power-generating authorities) before they are allowed to go into production. The photograph on page 112 shows the size and complexity of the apparatus needed for such tests, and at least hints at the costs involved. But the quality of insulators largely determines the reliability of a country's whole power supply, and the cost of rigorous testing, though high, is negligible compared with what the cost of power failure might otherwise be.

High-Temperature and High-Frequency Insulators

Although excellent for insulation at power frequencies, porcelain is far from being the ideal insulating material where high frequencies, or high temperatures, or both, are involved. With increasing temperature, as we have already seen, its conductivity rises steeply; at higher and higher frequencies it transforms more and more electrical energy into heat, with a corresponding loss of power. Yet ever since the beginnings of large-scale power production there has been a growing need for electrical insulation at high temperatures in all kinds of things, from domestic heaters to electric furnaces; and such modern means of communication as radio, television, and radar have created a vast demand for effective high-frequency insulators. Ceramists have therefore had to develop new materials with the requisite electrical properties.

Prominent among the devices demanding new insulating

materials was the spark plug. Not only must a spark plug produce a spark at each cycle of the engine by means of a high-frequency high-voltage discharge between two metals points, but it must also operate at a high temperature and stand up to considerable mechanical stress, including constant vibration. As internal combustion engines improved, the early porcelain spark plugs were no longer good enough, but by then ceramists were beginning to develop alumina ceramics, which are now the most widely used of all new ceramic materials.

In their latest form for spark plugs, alumina ceramics contain between 95 and almost 100 per cent pure alumina (Al_2O_3). The natural crystalline form of alumina, corundum, is very nearly as hard as diamond, and one slightly impure form, sapphire, is in a comparable price range. The alumina powder used in spark plugs is produced from the more common mineral bauxite, the naturally occurring hydrated form of alumina. Since the powder is extremely hard and has no plasticity, a little clay or artificial plasticizer such as wax is usually mixed with it to facilitate shaping. Among the shaping methods commonly employed are extrusion, followed by lathe-turning, and isostatic pressing (which is described in Chapter 6). Firing of alumina spark plugs is carried out at temperatures of 1600°C or more. Very-high-purity-alumina ceramics may be fired at temperatures as high as 1800°C, those with a considerably lower alumina content at temperatures not greatly exceeding 1400°C. Modern alumina products, with

Stages in making an alumina ceramic spark plug. Left: the blank made by isostatic pressing as described on page 163. Center: the blank after machining and firing. Right: the complete component.

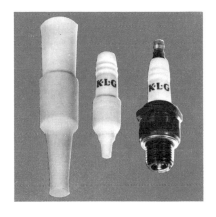

densities up to 50 per cent greater than that of porcelain, are among the strongest and hardest of all ceramic materials. They also have a higher dielectric strength (puncture strength) than porcelain and, at temperatures such as those encountered in a car engine, their volume resistivity is enormously greater.

All means of communication that depend on the transmission of power without wires must necessarily make use of radio frequencies, which at the lowest are thousands of times greater than power frequencies and at the highest many million times greater. Yet in the influence of an alternating electric field any insulating material will transform some electrical energy into heat, and in general, the higher the frequency the more the insulator will hot up. In high-frequency heating this transformation is made use of, but in radio-communications it simply represents a loss of power. The more power an insulating material dissipates as heat, the greater is its power factor, and the power factor of orthodox porcelain is too high to make it suitable for high-frequency insulation. If insulating materials with a far lower loss of power had not been developed, radio communications could hardly have grown to the colossal extent they have done in the past few decades.

The first of the important low-loss ceramics, as they are called, was steatite, which had already been used in Germany for low-frequency insulators of high mechanical strength, shaped to fine dimensional limits. In steatite ceramics, a high proportion of steatite (a natural crystalline form of magnesium silicate, or talc) is mixed with far smaller proportions of clay and some flux or fluxes other than the usual ceramic flux, feldspar. Feldspar is excluded because it contains the oxides of sodium and potassium, the alkalis that are responsible for the rather high dielectric loss of ordinary porcelain. The flux that normally replaces it is barium carbonate (constituting about 10 per cent of the body mix), though magnesium carbonate is sometimes used instead.

Most steatite electrical products are fairly small and are most commonly shaped by dust-pressing, but because the body contains little clay the ceramist adds artificial plasticizers such as waxes or polyvinyl alcohol. Firing at temperatures of 1350°c produces a glassy bond that holds all the particles firmly together, but the glass, of course, contains no alkalis to increase the power factor of the steatite. The fired products are at least as strong mechanically as ordinary porcelain.

Another of the important low-loss ceramics, developed since World War II, is zircon porcelain, a kind of porcelain in which quartz is replaced by zirconium silicate and feldspar by alkali-free fluxes. It has not only a low power factor, but also good electrical properties in general, and it is even stronger mechanically than steatite. Zircon-porcelain bodies contain enough clay to make them amenable to plastic shaping methods, as well as to powder-pressing, but because zirconium silicate is extremely abrasive, dies and tools used in shaping zircon porcelain must be made of abrasion-resistant tungsten carbide. Unlike most other low-loss ceramics, zircon porcelain has a wide firing range, which cuts down the risk of spoilage in the kiln. Firing is usually done at somewhere between 1300° and 1400°C.

In recent times alumina ceramics in extremely pure form, and containing virtually no flux, have come into increasing use for very-high-frequency insulation. Such products are heated to a temperature as high as 1800°C, which is sufficient to stick all the particles very firmly together but which, in the absence of fluxes, produces no glass phase, a process sometimes called *sintering*. Besides having a very low dielectric loss, these glass-free alumina ceramics have extremely good insulating properties, both at high temperatures and at high frequencies. The past few years have seen the development of translucent alumina ceramics that contain no micropores. Such materials are of great value in high-power, high-frequency valves, of which the envelopes can now be made of alumina instead of glass.

Radar and other electronic equipment in the rapidly expanding field of guided missiles, spacecraft, and aircraft must be housed in a radome or nose cone of some material that is transparent to high-frequency electromagnetic waves and that produces virtually no dissipation of power, otherwise signals would be weakened and distorted. In addition, the material must be able to withstand high temperatures and also great aerodynamic stress. High-purity-alumina ceramics have proved themselves suitable for applications of this kind.

134

Capacitors

So far we have been concerned primarily with insulators, but ceramics are also widely used in the manufacture of electrical capacitors. Early condensers, of the kind used in the radio receiving sets of the 1920s, consisted of metal plates separated by air. If high capacities were needed they had to be big and bulky because of the low dielectric constant of the air between the plates. (Dielectric constant, or relative permittivity, is a measure of the amount of electrical stress that a given amount of material will store.) If air is replaced by some material with a much higher dielectric constant, then it is possible to make less bulky capacitors with greater capacity. Many different materials have been used, including porcelain, mica, and paper. If the dielectric constant of air is taken as one, then that of porcelain is six to seven, and that of mica much the same. If miniaturization was to proceed, clearly much higher permittivities were needed.

Many modern high-permittivity ceramics are based on titania, mainly in the form of barium titanates or barium-strontium titanates. Titania itself (i.e. titanium oxide) has a permittivity

The band-casting process. Slip (red) is filtered through gauze (A) and fed onto a continuous stainless steel band (B). A sliding gate (C) determines the thickness of the cast film (D). Ceramic tape of controlled, consistent thickness down to 0.125 mm., which is used for making miniature capacitors, can be made by this process. Below, right: close-up of the ceramic tape coming off the machine.

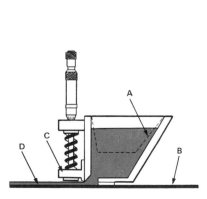 

about 10 times as great as that of porcelain, but some of the more complicated titanates have permittivities thousands of times as great. This, combined with their good insulating properties and low dielectric loss, has made it possible to produce extremely small capacitors of very high capacity for use at radio frequencies. Titanates, though important, are not the only high-permittivity ceramics. Others are based on zirconates and on stannites (i.e. compounds containing tin oxide).

High-permittivity ceramics have provoked the development of a whole new technology for the production of miniaturized capacitors. Ceramists have had to work out not only new and rigorous methods of controlling material purity and firing, but also new shaping techniques. One of these is the production of extremely thin (and evenly thin) flawless wafers of ceramic material in the form of continuous tape. The attachment of metal electrodes to these delicate wafers cannot be done by any such crude method as soldering, and the ceramist often employs vapor-deposition techniques. Sometimes it is necessary to encapsulate the finished capacitor in plastic, for protection.

Resistance Supports

Electrical ceramics have yet another important use, as supports for resistance elements. Where high resistances are used, perhaps in the form of a fine film of metal or carbon, and particularly where they are to operate at high temperatures, the support must have a very high resistivity, otherwise it will partially short-circuit the resistance element. Porcelains containing only alkali-free glass phases have been developed for such purposes.

High resistivity is only one essential property of a support for a heating resistance. Equally important is its ability to withstand continuous subjection to high temperatures—that is, its refractoriness. Refractory ceramics are the subject of the next chapter, but it is worth noting right away that all of them are required to have some specified property or properties in addition to refractoriness, simply because they all have a specified job to do at high temperatures. It is the great variety of jobs they must do that has led to such a wide range of materials being used in their manufacture.

5 Refractories and Industry

High voltage insulators, without which the distribution of electric power would be impossible, are strung out across the countryside for all to see. Refractories are mainly out of sight, and thus apt to be out of mind. Yet without them, all modern industries dependent on high-temperature processes would be put out of action. Among the long list of casualties would be iron and steel, glass, all steam-raising industries, nonferrous metals, gas, the production of lime and cement, and, of course, ceramics.

In the broadest sense we can regard common rocks and stones as refractory materials, but they are not good ones. They crack easily with sudden temperature changes and they do not lend themselves well to shaping. Even the earliest industrial heat processes, such as firing bricks and pots, making glass, and smelting ores, called for something better. It was probably bricks and pots that provided the clue to it. Both were made from abundant, easily-shaped clay; both had withstood high temperatures in the making; neither would burn or easily melt. So it was

Ceramic refractories at work. The lining of this 100,000-kg. electric-arc steel furnace (seen here being tapped) must be capable of holding molten metal at temperatures up to 2000°C. Chrome-magnesite walls and a roof of 15 per cent silica and 85 per cent alumina provide the resistance required.

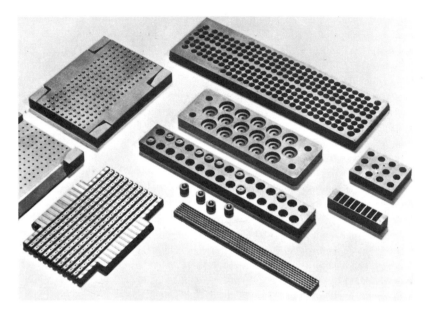

that as civilizations developed, well-fired clay bricks came to be the main materials used in the construction of kilns and furnaces, and clay the containers used for molten glass and metals.

Over the years increasingly complex industrial processes have made ever more exacting demands on the properties of refractories. To their early functions of containing fire or heat, as in furnace linings and boiler linings, and containing hot fluids, as in crucibles and scorifiers, has been added that of providing insulation at very high temperatures, as in kiln linings. They are needed in all shapes and sizes, from huge blocks of structural material and glasshouse pots two meters in diameter to fine pyrometer tubes and centimeter-high crucibles. Further, at elevated temperatures the rate of chemical reaction for most substances is enormously increased; refractories must therefore be highly resistant to reaction with any substance with which they will come in contact in service, not only so that they themselves will not easily deteriorate but also so that they will' not contaminate the products being manufactured. To meet all these demands ceramists now use a great number of materials that a

Opposite: Not all refractory products are enormous structural units. The largest of these machined graphite processing jigs used in making transistor components is less than 13 cm. in length.

Right: The fireclays from which most refractories are made are essentially complexes of alumina (Al_2O_3) and silica (SiO_2), which have melting points of 2050° and 1710°C respectively. Although, as shown here, the melting point of silica drops sharply with the addition of about five per cent alumina, in general, the greater the alumina content the, greater the refractoriness of the complex.

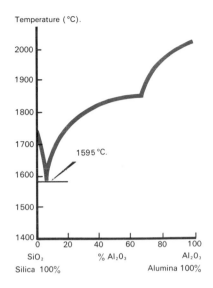

Temperature (°C).

2000
1900
1800
1700
1595 °C.
1600
1500
1400

0   20   40   60   80   100
SiO_2 % Al_2O_3 Al_2O_3
Silica 100%   Alumina 100%

few years ago would have been quite outside their domain, though they very often apply traditional ceramic techniques in handling them.

Fireclay

To this day, however, a greater proportion of refractories are made from clay than from any other material, the clays mainly employed being appropriately known as *fireclays*. The term was at one time applied only to underclays found in coal measures— that is, to the hard, compressed, refractory, and usually dirty clays that once formed the soil in which the tree-like ferns of the Carboniferous Period took root. Today the term tends to embrace any naturally occurring refractory clay, including some that are quite soft and plastic.

Fireclays normally consist of kaolinite ($Al_2O_3.2SiO_2.2H_2O$) together with some free silica (SiO_2) and anything up to 4 or 5 per cent of impurities, often including iron oxides and certain alkalis. If we neglect the H_2O of the kaolinite (which is driven off at about 600°c) and also the impurities, we can think of them essentially as complexes of alumina and silica, both of which have high melting points—silica 1710°C and alumina 2050°C. The melting point of an alumina-silica complex, however, depends on the proportions of the two components. The diagram on page 139 indicates that if we start with pure silica and then replace 5½ per cent of it with alumina, the melting point will drop from 1710° to 1595°C. It will not reach 1710°C again until the silica content is reduced to about 70 per cent and the alumina content increased to about 30 per cent. Thereafter, as the silica is further reduced and the alumina further increased, the melting point continues to rise in a fairly smooth curve, eventually reaching 2050°C when there is no silica and all alumina. Fireclays are more refractory than most other clays, largely because they contain more alumina and less silica than most other clays. In general the greater their alumina content the greater is their refractoriness.

Pure fired kaolin, which consists of 46 per cent alumina and 54 per cent silica, has a melting point of around 1750°C. Although there are bauxitic clays that have a higher alumina-silica ratio than this, the great majority of fireclays (since they usually contain free silica as well as kaolinite) have a lower one, and their melting points are therefore lower. In addition, the presence of iron oxide and alkaline impurities commonly decreases the temperatures at which fireclays will fuse.

A high proportion of refractories must serve also as structural materials, and in that case what matters in practice is not their simple refractoriness but their refractoriness under load. This is measured by subjecting the material under test to a specified compressive load under specified conditions, then heating it until it reaches the temperature at which it undergoes a required amount of deformation. (Loads, conditions, and amount of deformation specified vary from country to country.) The result is often expressed as the number of the standard pyrometric cone (see Chapter 1) whose squatting temperature is nearest to that at which the specified deformation occurs. Since the nominal temperature equivalents of pyrometric cones vary slightly according to whether Staffordshire, Orton, or Seger cone numbers are quoted, the figures for refractoriness throughout this chapter are given in degrees centigrade.

Aluminosilicate ceramic fiber, made up in the form of blanket, bulk, strip, and paper, can withstand temperatures up to 1300°C and serves a wide range of both refractory and insulating purposes.

Under compressive loads of 2 kg/cm², refractories made almost exclusively from naturally-occurring fireclays (or fireclays and bauxitic clays) will show 5 per cent deformation after 5 to 10 minutes' exposure to temperatures ranging from a little under 1500°C for those with a comparatively low alumina content up to about 1600°C for those which, fired, contain 42 per cent alumina.

A few of the uses of fireclay refractories are in blast-furnace tops and linings, lime kilns, cement kilns, ceramic kilns, gas retort settings, forge furnaces, aluminum melting furnaces, and domestic fire-backs. Hollow ware made of fireclay includes tubes for use inside furnaces, heating resistance supports, many special shapes used in heating by gas, and certain kinds of sagger— though, as we have seen, these are less important than they were a few years ago.

The composition and preparation of a fireclay body depends to a considerable extent on what it is to be used for and how it is to be shaped. Since fireclays vary not only in chemical composition but also in plasticity and degree of drying and firing shrinkage, the ceramist blends several of them to get the best combination of properties for the job in hand. More often than not he must also add some opening material to the body mix. In Europe this is usually a grog made by prefiring, crushing, and grinding a body of the same, or very similar composition; the proportion of grog is normally between 10 and 30° per cent, though in some cases it may be very much higher. In America the common practice is to use a proportion of flint fireclay, which is very hard and has practically no plasticity. The proportion and particle size of the opening material affect the drying shrinkage of the body and its resistance to thermal shock after firing; in general, the more grog contained in the body mix the smaller the shrinkage, the larger the particle size the greater the thermal shock resistance.

Shaping methods for fireclay bricks include extrusion and wire-cutting (often followed by re-pressing), stiff plastic or semidry pressing, and *tamping*, which consists of placing the semi-dry powder body in a mold and subjecting the top mold plate to repeated blows struck by a mechanical hammer. Refractories of complex shape are often produced by hand molding and slip casting.

After carefully controlled, and usually slow, drying in chamber driers or tunnel driers, fireclay refractories are fired in inter-mittent, continuous-chamber, or tunnel kilns, at temperatures ranging from 1200° to 1400°C. The precise firing temperature, as with other ceramics, depends partly on the refractoriness of the body and partly on how dense it is to be rendered.

Less Clay, More Alumina

We have seen that the refractoriness under load of even a super-duty fireclay brick does not commonly exceed 1600°C (even though its refractoriness when not under load is in the region of 1730° to 1760°C). Further, at high temperatures the load-bearing properties of fireclay refractories in general are on the low side, and their resistance to mechanical abrasions, unless they are especially treated, is only moderate. As suggested by the diagram on page 139, refractoriness can be improved by increasing the alumina content; this, at the same time, increases compressive strength and abrasion resistance. The ceramist produces these results by taking fireclay and adding to it one or more non-clay ingredients rich in alumina. These include sillimanite, kyanite, and andalusite, which are all naturally-occurring minerals of the general composition $Al_2O_3.SlO_2$, and alumina powder prepared by calcining bauxite (hydrated alumina). By such additions ceramists have built up a wide range of aluminosilicate refractories of steadily increasing refractoriness. The limiting case (which, of course, is logically outside the aluminosilicate range) is reached with the pure alumina ceramics already mentioned in Chapter 4.

The names given to refractories produced by adding alumina to natural clays are very confusing, due to the fact that they derive sometimes from the raw materials used, and sometimes from the chemical compounds formed during firing. In addition, names for very similar, though not always identical, types of refractory may vary from country to country. There are a few broad generalizations that should help, however. *Sillimanite refractories* is the name commonly applied to those in which sillimanite, kyanite, or andalusite form the major ingredient of the body mix. Those in which calcined bauxite is a major ingredient may be named from that ingredient, as in the term *bauxite refractories*. Another (overlapping) system of classification, however, relies solely on the alumina content of the body. In Britain all aluminosilicates containing more than 45 per cent alumina are classified as high-alumina refractories; in Western Europe there are two high-alumina classifications, 46 to 58 per cent alumina, and more than 58 per cent alumina; in America there are several classifications, going mainly in 10 per cent intervals from approximately 50 per cent minimum to approximately 80 per cent minimum.

Yet another name depends on the amount of mullite ($3Al_2O_3.2SiO_2$) formed during firing. The importance of mullite in a refractory is that it is the only alumina-silica compound that remains stable at very high temperatures, neither melting nor showing any noticeable reaction until a temperature of 1810°c is reached. In fact every alumina-silica complex will form some mullite when fired to temperatures exceeding 1200°c, but the actual amount formed does not depend only on the firing temperature and the ratio of alumina to silica; it is also influenced enormously by the form in which both components are introduced, and by the kind and quantity of impurities present. Thus it actually happens that one refractory body containing 68 per cent alumina and 27 per cent silica produces nearly 89 per cent mullite when fired, while another containing 71 per cent alumina and 23 per cent silica produces less than 35 per cent mullite when fired. It is therefore thoroughly understandable why ceramists designate some refractories as mullite refractories, others not. Good mullite refractories usually have a mullite content of 80 per cent or more, the average probably being somewhat nearer to 90 per cent. They are made mainly from sillimanite and kyanite, so that the terms *sillimanite refractory* and *mullite refractory* are sometimes interchangeable. Refractories made by adding calcined bauxite to fireclay, even though they may have just as high (and possibly even a higher) alumina content, very often have a far lower mullite content when fired.

In the latter category are high-alumina bricks, which may contain anything from 50 to 80 per cent alumina. The cost of the calcined bauxite needed to bring about this level, together with higher firing costs (since they may have firing temperatures of around 1500°C), makes such bricks much more expensive than fireclay bricks, but they are serviceable in certain situations where fireclay would fail. Those of the best quality have a refractoriness of about 1850°C and a refractoriness under load of around 1650°C. Often, too, they have a lower porosity than fireclay bricks, which makes them more resistant to penetration by *slag*, the refuse separated from all metals during the smelting process.

Sillimanite refractory bodies are prepared by calcining raw sillimanite or kyanite at temperatures in excess of 1500°C, crushing and grinding it to the required particle size, and mixing it with enough fireclay and water to render it workable. The higher the proportion of sillimanite or kyanite, the greater is the refractoriness, and the higher the cost. Where the refractoriness required is not much higher than that of good fireclay, the proportion of sillimanite may therefore be as low as 40 per cent, but for special quality ware it may exceed 95 per cent. Sillimanite refractories, which have a refractoriness ranging from 1750° to

These crucibles are made of recrystallized alumina, an impermeable refractory produced by sintering pure calcined alumina at high temperature. This gives a pure oxide material with an alumina content of 99.7 per cent and a maximum working temperature of around 1900°C.

1920°C and a refractoriness under load ranging from 1590° to around 1700°C, are used as construction materials (sillimanite bricks) on the regenerators and superstructures of glass furnaces, in the hot zones of cement kilns, and in certain ceramic kilns, notably those in which sillimanite refractories themselves are fired at temperatures ranging from 1500° to over 1700°C. Other important sillimanite products include pyrometer tubes and crucibles still used occasionally for melting optical glass.

Nearing the alumina end of the aluminosilicate range of refractories are those made from a very high proportion of fused pure alumina bonded with a little refractory clay. Bodies for alumina bricks, or corundum bricks, usually contain upward of 80 per cent electrically fused ground alumina mixed with up to 20 per cent fireclay and just enough water to produce a damp powder that can be shaped by tamping. Fired at temperatures of 1300°C or more, they have a higher refractoriness than either sillimanite or bauxite bricks, good load-bearing properties, and great resistance to both oxidation and reduction at high temperatures. Their resistance to *spalling* (cracking and breaking of corners) and to slag penetration, however, is somewhat low. They

Many refractory units are installed raw and then fired in situ. Here site-cast burner tunnels are being set in position in a boiler furnace. The rest of the wall will be covered by rammed refractory, also fired in position.

are used in burner blocks for high-temperature furnaces fired by gas or oil and also for muffles in many ceramic kilns and vitreous enamel kilns.

The alumina end of the aluminosilicate range, is reached in the pure or almost pure recrystallized alumina ceramics of the kind used in spark plugs (Chapter 4). In addition to their great mechanical strength, high dielectric strength, and resistance to thermal shock, such ceramics can withstand continuous working at temperatures in the region of 1900°C.

Silica Refractories

At the opposite extremity of the aluminosilicate range are refractories containing a very high percentage of silica and little or no alumina, since the inclusion of 5½ per cent alumina would reduce the melting point by over 160°C. Beds of ganister and quartzite that contain over 97 per cent silica and under 1 per cent alumina are common, and provide the main raw material. The only additives usually needed to produce a body for making silica bricks are lime (less than 2 per cent), about 3 per cent of a mineralizer, and enough water and plasticizer (often sulfite lye) to render the body capable of shaping by pressing, tamping, or hand molding. The lime serves as a bond for the silica particles in both the unfired and fired state. During firing, which is usually at 1430° to 1500°C, the mineralizer (often a frit containing iron oxide, soda, and silica) speeds up the conversion of the quartz into cristobalite and later tridymite, both of which are crystalline forms of silica, and stable at high temperatures.

Silica bricks can be used under load at temperatures up to 1650°C, do not shrink at high temperatures, and are resistant to thermal shock at temperatures from 600°C up to their melting point. The fact that they are also highly resistant to attack by iron oxide and acid slags makes them of special importance in the steel industry, and they are widely used in glass-tank furnaces, gas retorts, and coke ovens. Their weak point is that they are not very resistant to thermal shock at temperatures below 600°C.

Superduty silica bricks are of similar composition except that their flux content is more rigidly controlled, alumina and alkaline fluxes being almost eliminated and replaced by other oxides, such as lime, magnesia, manganese oxide, and zinc oxide. Such bricks can be used at temperatures up to 1700°C, and are less permeable to gases than ordinary silica bricks. In the roofs of open-hearth steel furnaces they give longer service than normal silica bricks, and they are often used in tunnel kilns where refractories are fired.

Basic Refractories

As mentioned earlier, it is essential that refractories should not react at high temperatures with the substances that will be in contact with them, and as a general guide to their properties in this respect ceramists classify them as acid, neutral, or basic. These classifications are not absolutely clear-cut, since at one end of the scale acid merges into neutral, at the other end neutral into basic. The whole aluminosilicate range yields only neutral and acid refractories, with the most strongly acid ones at the silica extremity, less acid ones in the fireclay and sillimanite groups, and the most clearly neutral ones at the alumina extremity. To produce basic refractories the ceramist moves right outside his home territory of aluminosilicates and relies largely on magnesium compounds. These include periclase (natural magnesia), magnesia produced from seawater, magnesite (natural magnesium carbonate), forsterite (which is magnesium orthosilicate, $2MgO.SiO_2$, most often found together with ferrous orthosilicate in the mineral olivine), and dolomite (which is naturally occurring double carbonate of calcium and magnesium). The refractoriness of all such compositions depends essentially on the high melting point of magnesia, which is 2800°c.

Magnesite refractories include those made from seawater magnesia as well as those made from natural magnesite. The preparation of magnesite refractories begins with calcining or "dead burning" the main raw material to drive off CO_2 from magnesite or H_2O from seawater magnesia, which is originally precipitated as $Mg(OH)_2$. The almost pure magnesia that remains, when cooled, crushed, and ground, constitutes from 80 to 95 per cent of the unfired refractory body. The rest consists of small quantities of some binding agent, such as lime, coal, ash clay, or tar, and usually a small percentage of iron oxide (which may have been present in the original magnesite). Around 2 to 3 per cent of water is added before the body is mechanically pressed into the required shapes at pressures exceeding 700 kg/cm².

Magnesite bricks made in this way have little mechanical strength before they are fired, and need the support of other refractory materials when they go to the kiln. The supports are often silica bricks, in which case some neutral refractory must be introduced between the acid silica bricks and the basic magnesite bricks resting on them. Firing is considerably slower than for building bricks, and the firing temperature is around 1500°c.

Bricks of this kind have a refractoriness of up to 2200°c if

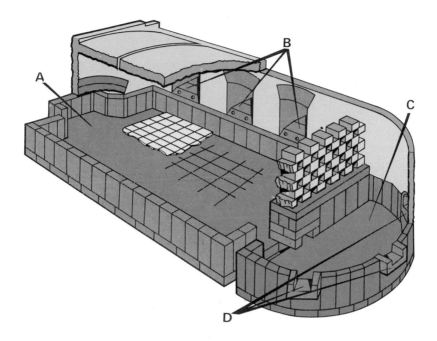

Typical glass tank furnace showing the complex system of refractories used. Raw materials enter at A, and are heated by burners (B) to approximately 1500°C. Molten glass is drawn off from forehearth (C) through feeders (D) for forming. Refractories used are: 96 per cent silica (blue), sillimanite (60 per cent alumina) (pink), and fusion-cast alumina-zirconia-silica (approximately 50 per cent alumina, 32-42 per cent alkali-resistant zirconium oxide) (gray). Zircon (65 per cent zirconia) (yellow) is used for the tank floor paving.

of a high quality. And they also have excellent resistance to basic slags. These qualities make them particularly useful in the construction of basic open-hearth furnaces as well as for lining surfaces in which lead, tin, or copper are refined. One of their weaknesses is their high thermal expansion, which may result in cracking when they are subjected to sudden changes of temperature. This, and the resultant tendency to cracking, can be reduced by adding a few per cent of alumina to magnesite bodies.

Many countries have an abundance of natural dolomite, a mineral with a melting point around 2300°c. Yet it is only in the last quarter of a century that it has been at all widely exploited as a refractory material. The difficulty about using it is that when it is calcined, and its CO_2 content driven off, what remains is a mixture of magnesia and lime; and the lime very easily hydrates in the presence of atmospheric moisture, causing products made from the mixture to disintegrate. However, provided they are protected from moisture before going into service, bricks made almost wholly from calcined dolomite can be usefully employed in basic open-hearth furnaces, certain types of cement kiln, and electric steel furnaces, where they will be subjected only to a dry atmosphere. Short-term pre-service protection can be provided by coating such bricks with tar. A better alternative, though it increases costs, is to add some siliceous material to the calcined dolomite during manufacture. This combines with the lime to form one or more calcium silicates that will not hydrate.

Olivine refractories are made almost entirely from crushed and ground uncalcined olivine rock; forsterite refractories are commonly made from olivine, magnesia, and small quantities of a binder to add mechanical strength to the unfired body. Both have high refractoriness under load, low thermal expansion, high resistance to thermal shock, and outstanding resistance to molten iron and silicates. They are of particular importance for wall facings and arches of regenerative furnaces used in the glass industry, for the lining of lime and cement kilns and of kilns used for calcining magnesite and dolomite, and for the roofs of copper furnaces. Both will deteriorate badly in service if they are in direct contact with such acid refractories as silica and fireclay at high temperatures.

Chrome and Chrome-Magnesite

The problem of keeping acid and basic refractories out of direct contact with each other is a very real one in industry. As already mentioned, it arises in the refractories industry itself when silica bricks are used as supports for magnesite bricks in the kiln. The diagram on page 149 shows how acid and basic refractories are used in close proximity in a glass-melting tank furnace. In all such cases it is vital that some neutral refractory should be interposed between acid and basic refractories. There are also some industrial processes in which neutral refractories are to be preferred to either basic or acid ones.

The neutral refractories at the alumina end of the aluminosilicate range are, in general, too costly for large-scale structural use. Less expensive ones can be made of chrome iron ores, multiple oxides of chromium, aluminum, iron, magnesium, silicon, and calcium, with the first four (and more especially the first two) greatly predominating. At one time neutral refractories were commonly made from such ores, the only other ingredient being a small proportion of some binder. Their main defects were their comparatively low refractoriness under load and their liability to crack with thermal shock.

Over the past thirty years or so ceramists have developed a wide range of refractories made from chrome ore and calcined magnesite, the neutral ones in which chrome predominates being termed *chrome-magnesite*, the slightly basic ones in which magnesite predominates being termed *magnesite-chrome*. Chrome-magnesite refractories are in general more resistant to thermal shock than magnesite and have a higher refractoriness under load than chrome. Besides serving to separate basic from acid refractories, they are used as structural materials in furnaces handling lead, copper, and aluminum.

Carbon Refractories

At 3550°C, carbon (which is a ceramic material only because it is widely used by ceramists in making refractories) has by far the highest melting point of all common elements. As far back as the early 19th century Sir Humphry Davy made use of its refractoriness when he produced a high-voltage arc discharge between two carbon rods and created a temperature high enough to burn a diamond. One moral of the Davy story is that if a diamond will oxidize at a sufficiently high temperature, so will other and less exalted forms of carbon. This means that when carbon is exploited as a refractory material its main sphere of usefulness is in places and processes where there is a reducing atmosphere, though it can also be used, with a shorter expectation of life, in slightly oxidizing atmospheres. This gives it a wide scope in many high-temperature processes, and carbon now provides

153

Above: 96 of these giant carbon refractory blocks were used to build the largest carbon bottom ever installed in a steel blast furnace. The blocks, largest of which weighed about 3600 kg., were keyed in place with carbon rods and joined with carbonaceous cement to form the 2.5-m.-thick, 10-m.-diameter hearth. Large size of blocks results in maximum radial transfer of heat by eliminating the "thermal dam" effect of numerous joints.

Opposite: Natural graphite, bonded with plastic fireclay or ball clay and shaped by normal ceramic techniques, is widely used to make crucibles, such as those shown here, for melting nonferrous metals (brass, aluminum, copper) and steel.

the basis of an increasingly important group of refractories. They are commonly made from carefully selected cokes, which are crushed and ground and then mixed with a small proportion of hot pitch or tar to facilitate shaping. Where the refractory is likely to encounter attack by acids in service, some 10 per cent of the coke may be replaced by anthracite. Large carbon blocks such as those illustrated on page 153 are usually shaped in large wooden molds, the carbon body being rammed in hard with pneumatic hammers, while smaller special shapes are more often made by dry-pressing methods. After setting and hardening, which may take anything up to four or five days, depending on size, the blocks are very slowly fired to a temperature of around

1000°C. During the process they are usually embedded in a thick layer of crushed coke and covered with fireclay or refractory mortar. Carbon blocks and bricks made in this way have high thermal conductivity and resistance to thermal shock, and high refractoriness under load. They are employed in the stacks, hearths, and melting zones of blast furnaces, in furnaces used for melting many iron alloys, and as linings of aluminum pots. Special shapes are used, for example, as molds for casting iron alloys.

Carbon refractories of the kind so far described are porous. The degree of porosity can be controlled to a large extent by the choice of raw materials and the particle size to which they are ground. Bodies of exceptionally low porosity (as low as 2 per cent) are made by special processes utilizing bituminous coal instead of coke. Graphite refractories, which are harder and have a higher refractoriness than ordinary carbon refractories, are commonly produced by reheating carbon bodies in an electric kiln to temperatures at which the amorphous carbon is converted into the crystalline form known as graphite. Among the many highly-specialized uses of graphite refractories is the making of self-lubricating piston rings and molds for machine-tool casting. Natural graphite bonded with plastic fireclay or ball clay, shaped by normal ceramic techniques, and very often glazed to prevent oxidation, is also widely used in making crucibles for melting brass, aluminum, copper, and steel.

Silicon Carbide

All the refractory materials so far mentioned occur in nature, though seldom in a form that the ceramist can use without a great deal of preliminary processing. Only in comparatively recent years have ceramists begun to make and use materials that nature does not supply in any shape or form. Among those of special use as a refractory is silicon carbide, made by mixing pure silica sand with high-quality coke and sawdust, and heating the mixture (usually in a carbon-resistance electric furnace) to a temperature approaching 2500°C. In the process the silica is reduced to silicon, which combines with the carbon to form silicon carbide; the sawdust, which burns out, serves to keep the mixture porous so that gases can easily escape from it.

Because of its extreme hardness, silicon carbide may constitute a very high proportion of the content of ceramic abrasives used for making grinding wheels. Because its refractoriness is high, its thermal expansion low, and its resistance to thermal shock good (and also because its resistivity is somewhere between that of a conductor and that of an insulator) it can be used as an electric heating resistance at temperatures far above those at which metal resistors would fail. The fact that it remains inert at high temperatures enables it to be used as a component of many kinds of refractory bodies without reacting with other components. Thus plastic fireclay and silicon carbide are mixed to produce refractory bricks that, owing to the low thermal expansion of the silicon carbide, are highly resistant to cracking, as well as to mechanical abrasion and acid attack.

Bodies composed of fireclay and silicon carbide, or graphite and silicon carbide, are used to make crucibles of very high thermal conductivity, a property that results in considerable fuel saving in this context.

Heat-Insulating Refractories

Where refractories are used mainly as heat insulators, low thermal conductivity and low heat capacity are the properties of paramount importance. Heat capacity is the product of weight times specific heat. The specific heat of the material depends on its chemical composition, and this the ceramist cannot alter very much without changing the way in which the refractory will react with other substances at high temperatures. But he can alter the weight per unit volume simply by making the refractory more or less porous. If he makes a given refractory 50 per cent porous instead of completely dense he will reduce its heat capacity per unit volume by approximately a half. It must also be remembered that all solid materials are better conductors of heat than air, so that when the ceramist increases the porosity (and thus the air-content) of a refractory he is also reducing its thermal conductivity. If the pores are too big, however, or if they form too many systems stretching continuously through the whole thickness of the product, a good deal of heat may be transferred by radiation and convection. For high-temperature insulation, therefore,

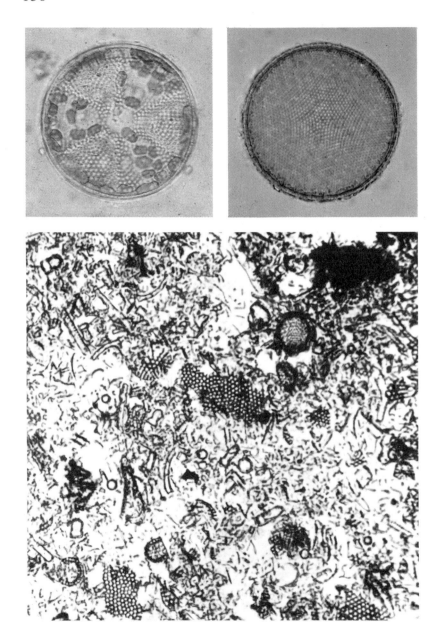

the aim is to produce lightweight, highly porous refractories in which the pores are very numerous, very small, and mostly sealed. This is commonly achieved by including considerable quantities of some fine material such as sawdust in the refractory body-mix, which will burn out in the kiln and leave pores. By such methods refractories with up to 80 per cent porosity can be made, some of which weigh as little as 544 kg/m³.

In some parts of the world, notably Denmark, the United States, and France, nature provides raw materials with built-in pores, which ceramists can use in the production of insulating refractories. These are diatomaceous earths, formed from the siliceous shells of minute single-cell organisms that bred in seas that have long since receded. Bonded with plastic clay, diatomaceous earths are used to produce extremely light-weight insulating refractories for use at temperatures up to about 800°C.

In practice two or three refractories may have to be teamed up to do one exacting job. For instance, the walls of a plant for a particular high-temperature process may need to have high bearing strength, high refractoriness, good resistance to, say, basic slag, and good insulating properties. Perhaps no single refractory will meet all these demands to the required degree. The answer may be to build a main wall with some dense material having good bearing strength but only moderate refractoriness and insulating properties and perhaps little slag-resistance. This can be backed and protected on the inside by some not very strong, but lightweight, slag-resistant, and insulating refractory. There will be a big drop in temperature through the thickness of the main wall. The covering of the outer surface of the main wall can then be a thickness of diatomaceous-earth refractory, which will give further excellent insulation at this lower temperature.

Where refractories are used to store and transfer heat, as in heat exchangers, the most important property required is high heat capacity. Here the product is made as dense as possible.

Opposite: The silicified remains of minute single-cell planktonic organisms (diatoms) provide the built-in pores that make diatomaceous earth an excellent material for insulating refractories. Opposite: top, photomicrographs of living marine diatoms (x 200); below, photomicrograph of diatomaceous earth found in Denmark, with fragments of diatoms clearly visible (x 350).

158

Refractory ceramic coatings can be applied to almost any base material by flame spraying. The coating material is passed through a flame on the spray gun and projected at high velocity onto a prepared surface to the required thickness. Ceramic coatings are increasingly used on metal components to protect them from corrosion, abrasion, erosion, and heat oxidation.

Pure-Oxide Refractories

The maximum working temperatures that refractories will withstand set a limit to what high-temperature processes can accomplish. Raising the working temperatures of refractories opens up new horizons of industrial achievement. One of the most promising ways of doing so is to make greater use of certain pure oxides.

The recognition that many pure oxides are excellent refractories dates back well into the 19th century. Lime (calcium oxide) showed its value as a refractory in limelights, where lime was heated to brilliant incandescence at temperatures around 2000°c. In the 1880s and 1890s, when gas lighting was coming up against

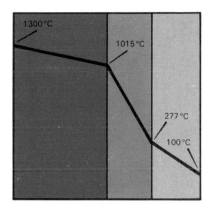

Two or three types of refractory are often teamed up to do one job. This cross section of a typical 0.5-m. furnace wall shows the three-stage temperature drop through refractory firebrick (red), light-weight insulating brick (pink), and ordinary red brick (gray).

increasing competition from electric lighting, great efforts were made to increase the illumination available from a given consumption of gas in a given time. The most successful method was to impregnate a seemingly flimsy cotton-fabric mantle (which nevertheless had to stand up to high temperatures for many hundreds of hours) with various oxides. The best combination proved to be a mixture of 99 per cent thoria and 1 per cent ceria, which gave a 20-candle-power illumination for 1 hour from 30 liters of gas. It is interesting that thoria has the extremely high melting point of 3050°C.

In the past few decades ceramists have turned increasingly to pure oxides to provide high-temperature refractories, and in particular to alumina, magnesia, beryllia, zirconia, and thoria. Since these oxides also have wide applications outside the field of refractories, they are discussed in the next chapter.

6 "Special" Ceramics

Earlier chapters of this book have dealt with ceramics of kinds that are probably known to the reader, even if he does not commonly concern himself with how they are made. We have seen how the range and scope of ceramic products have steadily increased almost from the beginnings of civilization, for domestic purposes, in building, and for industry. The technical products we have already met, such as insulators, capacitors, spark plugs, and the like, are now common enough, although in the long history of ceramics they are comparative newcomers. What the average reader cannot be expected to know is the colossal variety of entirely new ceramic materials that have been developed during the past 10 or 20 years to meet the ever more stringent demands of sophisticated modern industry.

For want of a better name, these materials, which touch 20th-century living at almost every point, are often called "special" ceramics. They are so different from traditional materials that they compel us to redefine the very word *ceramics*. At one time

Ceramics in the jet age. As airspeeds approach six or seven times the speed of sound, kinetic temperatures of up to 2000°C can be generated on leading edges of wings and engines. Heat-resistant ceramic coatings may well prove the solution to this problem.

we could say that a ceramic article was made substantially of clay, first shaped, then heated until it became hard and durable. For quite a long time, however, ceramists have manufactured certain products, particularly refractories, containing little or no clay; and most of today's special ceramics are entirely free from clay. It is tempting now to say that a ceramic material is any inorganic substance, usually a compound, never a metal, frequently an oxide. But even that broad definition breaks down with a material like carbon, which is in fact called a ceramic because of its highly refractory nature rather than because of any intrinsic characteristic relating it to other ceramic materials. In fact it is no longer possible to define ceramics in terms of composition at all. Instead they must be defined as inorganic materials that may be manufactured in a certain way, the essential part of which is the application of heat in one form or another, at one stage or another, to render them hard and resistant to their environment.

The great diversity of new materials has called not only for

New ceramic materials demand new forming techniques, such as this isostatic press for making ceramic spark plug insulators. Spray-dried 95 per cent alumina powder enters by the pipe at left and is then formed into a dense, uniform compact in the central pressure vessel. The blank then passes to the multispindle forming machine in the foreground, which machines it to required dimensions. This unique, fully automatic machine presses and machines insulators at the rate of 400 per hour.

revised definitions but also for changes and innovations in processing methods. Such techniques as jollying, jiggering, and slip-casting, on which pottery is based, are not commonly used in shaping special ceramic products. More frequently they are made by dry-pressing techniques, followed by heating while under pressure, or by hot-pressing—that is, shaping preheated or cold material in hot dies. Yet another process is isostatic pressing, which in its simplest form consists of filling a rubber bag with a finely powdered ceramic material, sealing the bag, then completely immersing it in a liquid contained in a pressure vessel. The pressure is then raised to several hundred kg/cm^2 for a short time. Since the pressure of the liquid is exerted equally in all directions, this process produces a very dense and uniform compact, ready for machining and firing.

A short chapter of this kind cannot begin to present a detailed account of even a small proportion of special ceramics, but it can, perhaps, give a useful picture of the more important ones, and the part they play in our modern technology. At the risk of oversimplifying what is essentially a complex subject we can divide the new ceramics into four groups, less according to their composition than according to their general characteristics and applications. One group, which we may call *engineering ceramics*, is of value mainly for its mechanical properties; a second is of interest for very specialized refractory behavior; a third, essential in the communications industries, has outstanding electronic properties; a fourth is particularly important in the generation of atomic power. We shall see, however, that these groups are just groups, and not watertight compartments. For instance, certain materials used in the manufacture of electronic components required to operate at extremely high temperatures belong as much to the second group as to the third. There are also a number of subgroups hard to categorize, such as the permeable ceramics used in the production of filtration media.

Porous ceramics have been put to practical use for quite a long time, one of the earliest examples being the development of the Pasteur filter made from porous porcelain, with which Louis Pasteur was able to isolate microbes. These are still made, and indeed ceramic bacteriological filters are still quite important.

Fitting porous ceramic tiles into the floor of a silo for use in the fluidized bed technique. Air is diffused through the tiles under pressure; powder in the silo then becomes fluidized and can be conveyed or blended in much the same way as a liquid. Many types of powder, from flour to fly ash, are handled in this way. The silo in the photograph is for handling powders used in the manufacture of plastics.

But the range of applications for permeable ceramics has now widened enormously, and a considerable number of such materials, each with its own carefully controlled pore size, are available for various purposes. These include separating dust from gases, removing solid particles from liquids, and purifying water in areas where pure mains water is not available. Permeable ceramics are also used in atomic power stations and in the bulk handling of powders for the fluidized bed technique. This technique consists essentially of blowing small jets of air into a powder. Provided the speed of air movement, size of jets, and particle size of the powder are all correct, the powder will behave just like a liquid; it can be pumped around a circuit, and it will pour along channels, just as water does. The fluidized bed technique is widely used now in the food industries, in the disposal of fly ash in power stations, and for putting plastic coatings on metal parts.

Alumina and Other Oxides

Many of the special ceramics are oxides, some are nitrides and carbides, and there are, in addition, some silicates and sulfides; probably the biggest single group are the oxides, however, particularly alumina, magnesia, zirconia, and beryllia. Alumina has been called "the engineering ceramic par excellence," and this is probably a fair statement. The ceramist uses the word *alumina* to describe not one material but a whole range, varying in purity, texture, and use. Lower grades of alumina, such as those containing from 85 to 95 per cent Al_2O_3, are generally manufactured by extrusion, pressing, or casting, sometimes with the addition of small quantities of clay or other plasticizer to make them easier to handle. They have moderately good mechanical properties and are frequently used where extreme mechanical requirements are not called for, as in thread-guides in the textile industry. Such materials are usually fired at temperatures not much above 1400°c, and generally have a cross-breaking strength of some 3000 kg/cm². But the need for better mechanical properties, and more especially for better electrical properties, has led to the production of purer aluminas that are less easy to shape and need to be fired at far higher temperatures. Ceramists have recently made progress in the shaping of extremely pure aluminas containing perhaps less than 1 part in 10,000 of impurity.

As mentioned in the last chapter, alumina is a highly refractory material, and to shape and subsequently sinter it is quite a

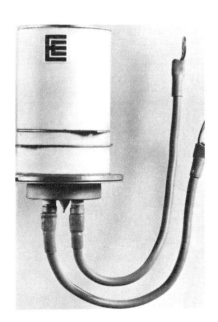

Envelopes for electron tubes, like this hydrogen-filled thyratron for use in compact radars, are now frequently made of high-purity, translucent alumina instead of glass. This is partly because of its greater strength, partly because of its better electrical and dielectric-loss properties.

difficult technological problem. When such a material is made, however, provided the grain size of the alumina is not too great, very high mechanical strengths by ceramic standards are obtainable. Cross-breaking strengths approaching 7000 kg/cm^2 (i.e. a tensile strength of something like 3000 kg/cm^2) have been obtained with these materials, enabling them to be used under conditions of considerable mechanical loading. Alumina is, of course, also very hard and resistant to abrasion, and has found applications in bearings, in anti-abrasion rings and fittings in a variety of machines, and in pumps subject to chemical attack. Because alumina, like all ceramics, is brittle, however, great attention must be paid to the design of components that have to match other parts of a complex machine, including those of metal and plastics.

The most advanced of the aluminas is one that is translucent. It is translucent because it is made at extreme purity, and the manufacturing process is such that all internal closed pores in the system are eliminated. Such a material naturally has good electrical properties and can be used for electron-tube envelopes and various other applications where translucency is necessary. Modern high-power, high-duty electron tubes for large electronic circuits now usually have envelopes made of alumina instead of glass, partly because of its greater strength and partly because of its superior electrical and dielectric loss properties. Its very low loss characteristics also enable it to be used as a "window" in electronic devices such as klystrons, a window being the route through which a radiation electron beam can pass while the vacuum is retained inside. Because of the very high refractoriness of alumina, advanced metallurgical industries use a great quantity of this material in the form of crucibles, furnace tubes, and sheaths for thermocouples.

In addition to all its other virtues, alumina is extremely hard, second only to diamond in Mohs' scale, and can be made into single crystals of high purity, which are in fact synthetic sapphires. Though these seem to have very little commercial potential as jewels, they are used to replace natural sapphires for bearings in high-precision instruments with moving parts. Since the change-over from the old 78 rpm gramophone records to modern long-

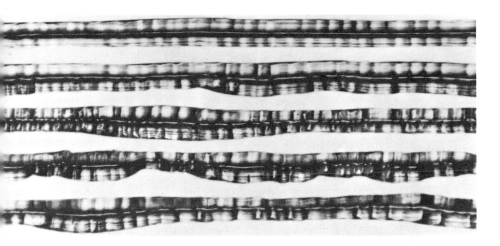

*These grooves on a stereophonic record (x 138) show the kind of
treatment gramophone needles have to sustain. Ceramics (usually titanate) with
special piezoelectric properties combine hardness with the necessary high
degree of sensitivity to convert minute variations in the groove into
corresponding fluctuations in electric current.*

playing disks with far narrower grooves, most of us have become
familiar with artificial sapphires as replacements for the old-
fashioned steel or fiber needles; but it is not always appreciated
that only a material of exceptional mechanical strength and
hardness could stand up to the continual and enormous vibra-
tions involved in traversing the varying zigzags in the groove.
The movements of the needle produced by the zigzags in the
groove have to be transformed into variations in an electric
current. For this purpose yet another ceramic is used, commonly
a titanate, which has piezoelectric properties. When such ceramics are subjected to pressure, an electric charge develops on their
surface, to an extent determined by the magnitude of the pressure.

More recently, but now in steadily increasing numbers, tools
for cutting and grinding metals are being tipped with alumina in
the form of synthetic sapphire, in place of the hard (but less
hard) materials formerly used, such as hard metals and tungsten
carbide. Alumina is, in fact, one of the most versatile of all
ceramic materials. By modifications in composition, additions of

168

mineralizers, variations in manufacturing technique, control of grain size, and alterations in firing temperature, alumina ceramics can be tailor-made to meet a wide range of industrial requirements.

Other oxide ceramics of growing importance are magnesia, zirconia, and beryllia. These are used chiefly because of their highly refractory properties, and thus find their greatest applications in the metallurgical industries. All of them have high melting temperatures (above 2000°C) and when used for making crucibles they are highly resistant chemically to most substances likely to be melted in them. Unfortunately they present greater difficulty in shaping and production than does alumina, and the range of products that can be made from them is therefore more restricted. One in particular, beryllia, can be highly poisonous during manufacture, and techniques must be carefully controlled to prevent the possibility of factory workers breathing beryllia powder. The general techniques of manufacture, however, follow normal ceramic practice. The material is ground into a fine powder, small additions of plasticizer or other mineralizers are

Beryllia (beryllium oxide) is remarkable among the oxide ceramics for its extremely high thermal conductivity. The graph shows how slip-cast (black line) and hot-pressed (red line) beryllia are superior in this respect to other oxide ceramics such as magnesia (blue) and alumina (green). Whereas most ceramic materials have thermal conductivities well below those of metals, that of beryllia approaches that of high-purity aluminum (yellow) below its melting point (601°C).

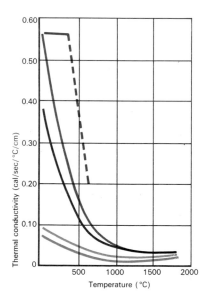

Cermets are composite mixtures of ceramics and metals, with properties combining the best of both materials. These three photomicrographs (all x 1500) show typical structures combining good cutting properties (provided by carbide ceramics) with toughness (provided by metals). Right: pale angular grains of tungsten carbide (WC), with small amounts of blue-green cobalt (Co) to provide a bond, give a cermet widely used for cutting tools and rock drills.

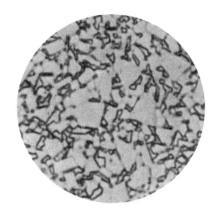

For machining steel, more complex mixtures using stronger ceramics are needed, such as this cermet of WC (pale and angular) and titanium-carbide-rich globular phase (orange) containing tantalum carbide (TaC) and WC, also bonded by Co (green).

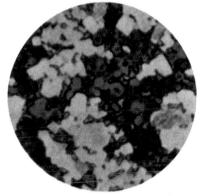

Cermets with high titanium carbide (TiC) content are prone to brittle fracture, but this new cermet has the TiC-rich globular phase bonded by nickel-molybdenum alloy, and combines TiC's good wear properties with a resistance to chipping previously unobtainable.

sometimes made, and the mixture is then pressed or extruded into the required shape. Firing, frequently at very high temperatures, is in some cases done under special conditions, as, for instance, in atmospheres of hydrogen or nitrogen.

Beryllia has one special characteristic that makes it an extremely interesting material for certain applications, namely its very high thermal conductivity. Nearly all ceramic materials have far lower thermal conductivities than metals, maybe 20 to 110 times lower, and although this is an advantage when they are being used for insulation, it does mean that they are frequently susceptible to thermal shock in environments where the temperature changes rapidly. Beryllia, however, has a thermal conductivity almost equal to that of metallic aluminum.

Carbides and Nitrides

Like alumina, magnesia, zirconia, and beryllia, the carbides too are highly refractory. They rank, indeed, among the most refractory materials known, and they are also extremely strong—almost as strong as the purest aluminas. Tungsten carbide is still widely used in cutting tools, because of its very great hardness, though pure alumina ceramics are largely replacing it. Boron carbide, one of the hardest of all materials, is used as an abrasive powder and to make die inserts for pressing steel. Silicon carbide finds its main use as a bulk refractory, but because it conducts electricity to a certain extent, it is also very useful for making heating elements required to operate at temperatures too high for ordinary wire elements. Such elements are very widely used at temperatures up to 1500°c.

All the carbides are limited in their uses—as, of course, are many other ceramics—by their brittleness; but carbides are also particularly prone to oxidation, which degrades their properties once temperatures much above red heat are reached. Silicon carbide is the least affected in this way, which explains why it can be used as a refractory support in high-temperature ceramic kilns and for heating elements. The reason for its better performance can to some extent be explained by the fact that, when it does oxidize, the silicon carbide is turned into silica. A protective layer of refractory silica thus forms on the surface of the silicon carbide, and this reduces considerably the effects of further attack by oxygen. Silicon carbide often has a small amount of clay added to it in order to improve its shaping characteristics, but, as is evident from the graph on page 139, this inevitably reduces its refractoriness. More modern techniques involve using some other compound of silicon, notably silicon nitride, as a bonding material. In small proportions, this acts as a very effective bond between the silicon carbide grains.

Silicon nitride itself is one of the newest and most interesting of ceramic materials. It is formed by the *nitriding* process, which consists of taking the element silicon, pressing it into the required form, and then heating to a temperature of about 1400°c in an atmosphere of nitrogen. The nitrogen then combines with the silicon to form silicon nitride, Si_3N_4, and the particles sinter together, giving a very strong, dense material. Since silicon nitride has very good thermal shock properties and is not wetted by molten metals, there are many applications for it in the metallurgical industries, as there are for aluminum nitride, another of the new materials. Perhaps the most important thing about silicon nitride is the way it lends itself to precise shaping and close dimensional control. If a silicon compact, which is weak, is partly nitrided, the resultant material can be machined, just as one would machine brass, into very elaborate shapes and to very close tolerances. Subsequent full nitriding, without affecting the shape of the article, renders it extremely strong, with a cross-breaking strength of 1400 kg/cm² or more. The interesting point is that there is almost no firing shrinkage when the material is thus fully nitrided, and in this way it differs from almost all other ceramic materials. As a result ceramic parts of high precision and complicated shape can be made without the need for very expensive post-kiln grinding processes such as are used for alumina, and for which it would be necessary to use diamond grinding. Silicon nitride has very good thermal shock properties, and pieces at temperatures of 1000°c can be thrown into water without coming to any harm. Because it can be machined, it can be used for nuts and bolts, and also for bearings that must operate at very high temperatures. Already it is in use in nuclear reactors and in the metallurgical industries; and while the full range of its

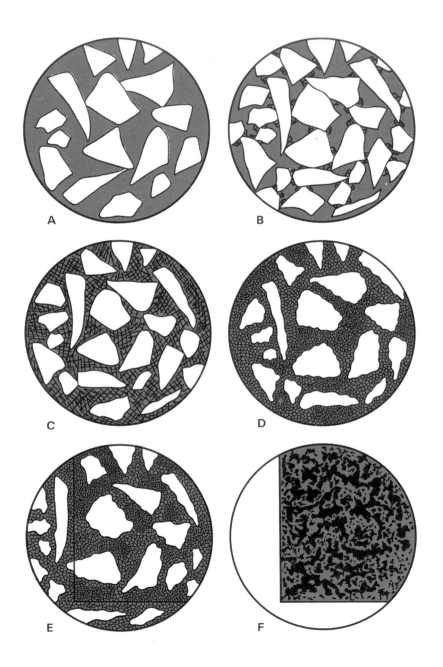

applications has yet to be established, there are clearly countless uses for it in components needed in many high-temperature processes. It may well be that silicon nitride will be one of the most important ceramics of the future.

Silicon nitride made in the way just described is known as *reaction-sintered* because the reaction for forming the material takes place during the sintering process. It is always somewhat porous, even though the pores are extremely small, leaving the material almost impermeable to gases and liquids. Nevertheless it *is* porous, and this reduces its mechanical strength. An alternative technique for forming silicon nitride is to hot-press it with additions of mineralizers such as metallic oxides. In this way an extremely dense nonporous material can be produced, with a hardness not much below that of diamond and a modulus of rupture probably exceeding that of any other ceramic material. In the hot-pressing process the powder is contained in a graphite die that is subjected to high pressures while in the electrical field of a radio-frequency generator that raises its temperature to between 1700° and 1800°C, and by this process only pieces of small size and limited complexity of shape can be made. Further machining can be done with diamonds, and possibly with lasers, though this is a very slow and expensive process. It is early yet to forecast the full potential of this form of silicon nitride, but there is already talk of using it for blades in high-temperature jet engines.

Opposite: formation of single-phase silicon nitride. Silicon powder (A) is isostatically pressed, causing weak friction-welding at junctions (B). Reaction with nitrogen begins at 1100°C at one atmosphere pressure, causing growth of Si_3N_4 to begin between particles (C). This chemical reaction is continued (D) to establish a strong mechanical bond by thickening of the silicon nitride skeleton. Reaction is suspended (E) and the partially reacted compact is machined to required shape to close tolerances. Reaction is then continued at progressively higher temperatures up to the melting point of silicon (1450°C), with no loss of dimensional accuracy, until the whole compact is converted to silicon nitride (F). The result is a material with excellent resistance to thermal shock and a cross-breaking strength of 1400 kg/cm² or more, which may well be among the most important ceramics of the future.

Jet Flight and Soluble Ceramics

Flying around the world at 1000 km/h is now commonplace, and speeds of several times that of sound are predicted for the near future. All this is due to the development of the jet engine in the late 1930s and during World War II, but it is seldom realized that the manufacture of a modern high-performance jet engine commonly depends on the behavior of very specialized ceramic materials. The efficiency of a gas turbine engine is bound up with the temperature at which it works: the higher the temperature, the greater the power output. This means that increasingly refractory materials have to be used for the thousands of blades required in every large modern jet engine.

Nickel-containing stainless steels are now the usual metals from which jet engine blades are made, but there is a limit to their refractoriness; if the blades are to be subjected to very high temperatures they must be cooled and prevented from melting by being made hollow, so that a constant stream of air can pass through them. In addition, they must be made to extremely fine tolerances, both internally and externally, otherwise the engine would be out of balance when the rotors went round at high speeds. To ensure that the internal shape and dimensions are exactly as required, the shape is first made to high precision in a very special ceramic material. Next the metal is cast around this preformed ceramic core, and finally the core has to be removed. Since the internal shape of the blade is reentrant, there is no possibility of simply pushing the core out whole. Originally it was removed mechanically—in other words, by knocking it out bit by bit. But as the structure and pattern of gas turbine blades became more and more complex this technique was found to be unsatisfactory and a range of soluble ceramic materials had to be developed.

Throughout this book, stress has been laid upon the permanence of ceramics, resulting from their composition and their firing treatment; yet here we have ceramics that can serve their purpose properly only by virtue of their impermanence. But that is by no means the only quality demanded of them. Not only must they be capable of being dissolved when they are no longer wanted, but they must also be highly refractory, since the stainless steels

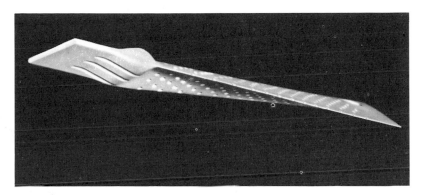

Preformed ceramic core for precision casting hollow gas turbine blading. In forming hollow air-cooled blades, cores are needed that can stand up to molten steels at over 1500°C and can be dissolved out from reentrant internal shapes by applying alkalis, or, in some cases, water. Special ceramics provide the ideal material for such cores.

are poured around them at temperatures of 1500°c or more. Further, their chemical composition must be such that they will not react with the hot metal, thereby embrittling the finished blade or otherwise spoiling its performance.

The ever-increasing complexity of turbine-blade design, coupled with ever-increasing demands for dimensional accuracy, has compelled ceramists to adopt new techniques in the shaping of preformed cores. Perhaps the most common one is injection molding, a process usually associated with the manufacture of plastics. In this process the nonplastic ceramic powders, which have to be of very carefully controlled chemical composition and particle size, are mixed with various plasticizers and binders and then extruded into high-precision molds of great complexity of shape. This technique has been developed to such an extent that complicated cores can now be made to accuracies of 1 or 2 parts in 1000 without any post-kiln machining. The nature of the composition of a core depends not only on what metal is to be cast around it but also on the technique that is to be used for removing it. The common practice is to use molten sodium carbonate or strong solutions of sodium hydroxide to remove the cores, but cores can also be made that will dissolve out with

Left: thimble filled with the 0.53-mm.-diameter ferrite cores used as memory cells in modern computers. These are magnetized and demagnetized at high speed by the application of electrical current to represent the "zeros" and "ones" of computer language. This thimbleful would be sufficient to memorize the average adult's vocabulary (between 60,000 and 80,000 words).

Below: Another application of ferrite has greatly reduced the size of telephone switchboards. Modern "solid-state" switching requires no mechanical moving parts, but operates by changing the electrical and magnetic characteristics of numerous miniature ferrite components.

hydrofluoric acid, with hydrochloric acid, or even, in some special cases, with water. Although preformed cores were developed in the first place to facilitate the making of aircraft engines, they are finding a growing range of applications in general engineering, wherever shapes with complicated internal passages are required.

As the speed of flight increases, the demands for engine performance increase with it, and at several times the speed of sound the conventional type of gas turbine engine with rotating parts is no longer suitable. Aircraft designers therefore use the ramjet engine, which is little more than a plain tube with a very high-temperature fire inside it. The temperature is such that no metal will withstand it, and ceramists are having to develop new refractory materials for the inside linings of such engines. What is perhaps more surprising is that for very high-speed aircraft the sharp leading edges of engines and wings will also probably have to be made of ceramic materials. This, again, is because metals will not withstand the kinetic temperatures of well over $2000°c$ that can be developed at flying speeds in excess of 6500 km/h.

Ferrites and Communications

The dramatic progress in flight over the past two decades has been matched, if not surpassed, by tremendous advances in communications. In this field the rapid developments in radio and television, the changed techniques employed in telephone services, and the increasing use of very-high-frequency and even ultra-high-frequency radio waves, have all forced ceramists to develop more and more specialized materials. In Chapter 4 we saw something of the importance of low-loss ceramics and high-permittivity ceramics in this context, but perhaps the materials that have made the biggest single impact on civilization in recent times are the magnetic ceramics, or ferrites. These, as one might expect, are based upon iron compounds, but they are so developed as to have very curious electrical properties. In one form or another they find a place in radio receivers, television sets, oscillators, pick-ups, telephones, and computers; and, of course, they can also be used simply to attract bits of iron and steel, in the same way as an iron magnet. Ferrites have a high electrical resistance, a very low electrical loss, and a much higher magnetic permeability than have metallic materials (i.e. their ratio of magnetic induction to the external field causing the induction is greater than that of metallic materials). They also work over a much wider range of frequencies than do orthodox metallic magnets. Ceramic magnets can be either soft or permanent, as can those of metal, and they can be made to reverse their magnetic characteristics under the impulse of an external electrical field. Both very small and quite large magnets are usually made by the standard processes of pressing or otherwise shaping the powdery material and then heating to temperatures approaching 1400°C in controlled atmospheres. A wide range of fired compositions now exists. Simple ferrites—that is, purely iron oxide compounds such as Fe_2O_3—were the beginning, but today most ferrites have spinel structures, and more complex ones such as manganese and zinc ferrites are obtainable. Changes in the state of oxidation of manganese and zinc ferrites produce marked changes in their magnetic properties, so that very great care has to be taken in the manufacture of ferrite materials. Barium ferrite, which is perhaps the commonest one, makes an extremely good permanent magnet.

A modern computer depends on thousands upon thousands of tiny ferrite elements that act as memory cells, and the basis of the operation consists of changing the magnetic field around these small elements. Ferrites have also been vital in revolutionizing relays in communications systems. In the old mechanical relay a current passing around a coil magnetized a metal center, which

Nuclear fuel pellets of uranium oxide. The bar in the foreground is about 7 cm. long. Uranium is used in this ceramic form as a nuclear fuel because it is more refractory than uranium metal (having a melting temperature of 2800°C), has no phase changes, and, unlike the metal, does not expand when irradiated.

thereby attracted or repelled a switching element. Modern systems, known as *solid-state switching*, do not require any mechanical moving parts; instead they depend entirely on changing electric and magnetic characteristics produced in a small piece of ceramic material when currents pass through it or in its vicinity. Thus the size of switching systems can be very considerably reduced and the speed of action enormously increased. Turning to yet another branch of modern communications we find that ceramic semiconductors, employed in transistors, have reduced the size, production costs, and running costs of radio and television sets. The cumbersome glass-envelope electron tube once common to all such sets not only took up a lot of space but also absorbed a lot of power, and was therefore not a very efficient device for converting radio signals into sound. A ceramic product, which takes up far less space and works with almost no power, has made possible the miniature transistor radio set and the portable television set.

Nuclear Power

The development of nuclear energy in its various forms, both as a military weapon and as a source of electric power, is one of the most important technical developments of this century. As in so many other branches of industry, we find that ceramics are necessary for its further advance.

The basic principle of a nuclear reactor for developing power is that the energy comes from the fission—that is, the breaking down—of nuclei of the uranium 235 atom, which occurs when it is bombarded with neutrons. This bombardment yields energy by means of a self-propagating reaction—that is to say, each time fission is produced by a single neutron, two or more fresh neutrons are released, which are then available for further fission. In this way energy becomes available from the nuclei as they are steadily broken down. All the early reactors used metallic uranium as the fuel—that is, the material subjected to fission. Natural uranium is not a single nuclear species. It contains two isotopes, one with an atomic weight of 238, the other with an atomic weight of 235, the latter being the rarer and comprising less than 1 per cent of the total weight of uranium. It is only this latter, U^{235}, that breaks down when neutrons hit it. Thus all the earlier reactors used the pure isotope uranium 235, which had to be carefully extracted from uranium metal, and most of the power reactors now running are based on this process. Metallic uranium has a number of disadvantages: First, it has a not particularly high melting point (1130°C), and since heat is generated during the process there is risk of the metal fuel element melting; secondly, fission releases certain gases (krypton and xenon) in the metal that cause it to swell and thus fail. Additionally there are two phase changes in the 700°C temperature region, each of which causes a swelling of the uranium metal. These size changes are a considerable technological disadvantage. Instinctively one turns to ceramics to see if uranium metal can be used as a ceramic compound. Ceramics are used in atomic energy for the same basic reasons as they are in other industrial fields, namely for their high refractoriness, their stability, and their great corrosion resistance; in addition they have a better resistance to radiation than do most metals.

The "ceramic" forms of uranium that can now be used for atomic reactors are either the oxide or the carbide. Other material such as thoria can also be added to the system. There are several oxides of uranium, but uranium dioxide (UO_2) is of most interest. It is very much more refractory than uranium metal, having a melting temperature of nearly 2800°C, which places it among the most refractory materials in existence. It has no phase changes and on being irradiated does not expand in the same way as the metal. On the other hand, if its temperature is raised to 400° or 500°C in air it further oxidizes to U_3O_8, which is unsatisfactory, and thus any reactor using uranium oxide as a fuel must enclose it in containers with a nonoxidizing atmosphere around it.

Perhaps the more interesting and more commonly used ceramic form of uranium is uranium carbide. As in the case of the oxides, there are a number of carbides, in particular uranium monocarbide and uranium dicarbide, illustrated in the photomicrograph

Opposite: Uranium carbide, with its greater mechanical strength and higher thermal conductivity, has advantages over uranium oxide as a nuclear fuel. Photomicrograph (x 200) shows a nuclear fuel consisting of uranium monocarbide (blue and green areas) and uranium dicarbide (white areas).

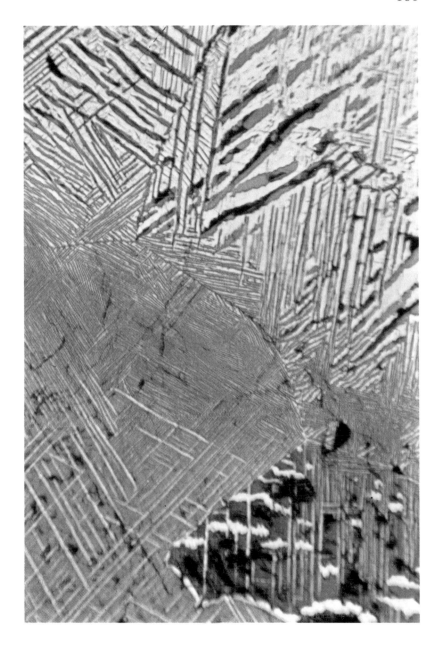

on page 181. The latter is not very stable, particularly in the presence of water, and it is the monocarbide that is used as fuel. It has a very high density and refractoriness and is mechanically stronger than uranium oxide. It is one of the strongest ceramic materials, if prepared at almost its true density and when it contains no pores. Another advantage the carbide has over uranium oxide is its higher thermal conductivity. While a reactor is running, the center of the fuel rod becomes hotter than the outside. A metal fuel has a high thermal conductivity and thus there are no severe temperature gradients in the fuel element. When ceramic materials with much poorer thermal conductivity are used, difficulties can arise, because the center of the rod may reach temperatures approaching the melting point of the ceramic material itself, and thus any improvement that can be obtained in the thermal conductivity of the fuel rod is of great value.

As has been seen earlier in this book, the poor thermal shock properties of many ceramics caused by their low general strength and fairly poor thermal conductivity have often proved a disadvantage in their engineering applications. Careful design is

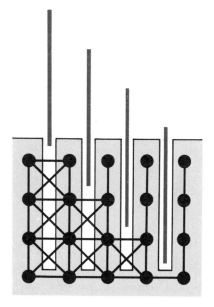

An important application of ceramics in the nuclear field is in the control rods. As shown here, these rods (red lines) are used to slow down or stop reaction by preventing neutrons (black lines) moving between the fuel elements (black dots). Only materials with high efficiency in capturing neutrons and with high thermal conductivity are suitable: Ceramics made from elements such as cadmium, boron, hafnium, gadolinium, and samarium are used.

Opposite: Batches of extruded montmorillonite clay like this one are used to absorb radioactive waste. The clay is then baked, permanently locking in the radioactive atoms.

necessary to take advantage of their good properties and to avoid stressing them dangerously. The same principles apply in atomic energy, and the thermal shock characteristics of fuel elements are quite important; when turning the reactor on or off, the elements can be subjected to very rapid temperature changes. Various suggestions for improving the thermal shock resistance of uranium carbide include making *cermets* in which metal is combined with uranium carbide, but anything published in this field runs the risk of being out of date before it gets into print, so rapid are the research developments in nuclear power. One thing is quite clear; the more efficient reactors of the future will need higher operating temperatures, and ceramic forms of uranium or maybe thoria will be used as fuel instead of the metal.

Another important possible use for ceramics is the container, known as the *can*, in which the element is mounted. In early reactors, using uranium metal as the fuel, the elements were generally sheathed in aluminum. As operating temperatures rose, the can had to be made of stainless steel, and in some of the latest reactors using ceramic elements it has been found that the best

Photomicrograph (x 350) of a ceramic can used in high-temperature gas-cooled nuclear reactors. The thorium-uranium dicarbide fuel particles in the center are contained in a layer of carbon (gray circle) and silicon carbide (white circle), which retains the fission products and suppresses swelling.

metal containers are probably not refractory enough, so ceramic cans are being developed to replace them. Ceramics such as alumina are clearly interesting, but in some ways the most promising material is beryllia. As already described, this is an oxide of the metal beryllium and is quite refractory. Its most important characteristic is its extremely high thermal conductivity, approaching that of metals. This makes it of very considerable interest as a canning material, because it enables heat to get away from the element inside and so reduces the thermal shock upon the fuel. Beryllia, as we have seen, can be highly poisonous during manufacture, and therefore requires extremely careful handling. It has, however, many good properties for use in this particular context, but it is of course brittle, and even with the best of modern ceramic manufacturing techniques, such as hot-pressing, it is not particularly easy to get the material pressed and fired to the high density required.

A third and important application of ceramics in the nuclear field is not in making the reactor go, but in stopping it—in other words, for making the control rods. These serve to prevent neutrons getting to the fuel element in a greater amount than is desirable. In this way they keep the reaction under control and if necessary can be used to stop all neutrons reaching the fissile material. For this purpose another group of chemical elements is needed, which must be highly effective in capturing neutrons; they are therefore said to have a high capture cross-section. Certain elements (some rather rare) such as cadmium, boron, hafnium, gadolinium, and samarium are useful for this purpose. They cannot, however, be used as metals and it is normal to convert them into what may be termed a ceramic form. They can be used as oxides, borides, carbides, and nitrides, and various patents exist for porcelain rods and also for special glasses containing these elements that are highly efficient in capturing neutrons. One difficulty is that they need to have extremely high thermal shock resistance, because while the reactor is running at full power its temperature will be quite high, and if it is necessary to stop it suddenly the rods have to be pushed into the system and subjected to an extremely high thermal shock, under which they must not fail. Thus the use of ceramics as shutdown material is still not entirely settled. Once again the deficiencies of materials have to be balanced against their useful properties and, as for fuel elements, more and more work is being put into producing suitable ceramics.

These are the main applications of ceramic materials in reactors. In addition, they play an important part as ancillary materials, for example in making crucibles and other containers used in the metallurgical processes for extracting pure isotopes.

The examples of the expanding application of ceramics in modern technology given in this chapter are by no means exhaustive. They serve however to show how one of the oldest industries in the world has adapted itself to serve the needs of modern industry—industry that could not have developed to nearly the same level without its constant aid.

Acknowledgments

Page 12 Photo English Clays Lovering Pochin & Co. Ltd.: 16 Royal Doulton Ltd.; photo Ken Coton: 19 (Top) The Director, British Ceramic Research Association (Bottom) F. H. Norton, *Ceramics for the Artist Potter*, Addison-Wesley Publishing Company, Reading, Massachusetts: 20 (Top) United States Travel Service, London (Bottom) Photo Mavis Ronson, from Paul Popper Ltd.: 24 Richard Sutcliffe Ltd., Horbury, Wakefield: 28 Redland Bricks Limited: 29 Redland Bricks Limited; photo K. Coton: 31 Redland Bricks Limited: 32 Royal Doulton Ltd.; photo K. Coton: 33 (Top) The Director, British Ceramic Research Association (Bottom) Photo Redland Bricks Limited: 37 The High Brooms Brick & Tile Co. Ltd., Tunbridge Wells: 38 Klaus Koch: 39 The Director, British Ceramic Research Association: 40 British Museum: 43 A. B. Searle & R. W. Grimshaw, *The Chemistry and Physics of Clay*, Ernest Benn Ltd., London: 44 (Top left, right) British Museum (Bottom) British Museum; photo B. Kapadia: 45 (Top left) British Museum; photo B. Kapadia (Top right, bottom) British Museum: 48 (Left) Josiah Wedgwood & Sons Ltd. (Right) British Museum: 49 British Museum: 53, 54 William Boulton Limited, Burslem, Stoke-on-Trent: 55, 58 Royal Doulton Ltd.: 59 Josiah Wedgwood & Sons Ltd.: 60 F. Moore, *Rheology of Ceramic Systems*, Maclaren & Sons Ltd., London: 62 Niro Atomizer Ltd., Copenhagen: 64 Royal Doulton Ltd.; photo B. Kapadia: 65 Photos Briglin Pottery: 67 (Top left) Josiah Wedgwood & Sons Ltd. (Top right) Service (Engineers) Limited, Cobridge, Stoke-on-Trent: 70 (Top) Royal Doulton Ltd. (Bottom) Hathernware Ltd., Loughborough, Leics.: 71 Josiah Wedgwood & Sons Ltd.: 72, 73 Royal Doulton Ltd.; photos B. Kapadia: 75 Villeroy & Boch, Mettlach, Saar: 77 Hopol Ltd., Sandbach, Cheshire: 80 Royal Doulton Ltd.; photo B. Kapadia: 81 Photos Lorenz Hutschenreuther, Aktiengasellschaft, Selb, West Germany: 82 Photo Shelley Furnaces Ltd.: 85 Royal Doulton Ltd.; photo B. Kapadia: 86 Josiah Wedgwood & Sons Ltd.: 88 Royal Doulton Ltd.; photos B. Kapadia: 91 Ferro Enamels Ltd., Wombourne, Wolverhampton: 96 Royal Doulton Ltd.; photos B. Kapadia: 99 Carter Tiles Limited, Poole, Dorset: 101 (Top left) Ernst Rosenthal, *Pottery and Ceramics*, Penguin Books, 1949 (Top right, Bottom) Photos Josiah Wedgwood & Sons Ltd.: 102, 103 Royal Doulton Ltd.: 104 Photo K. Coton: 108 (Top left) Photo Josiah Wedgwood & Sons Ltd. (Bottom) Royal Doulton Ltd.; photo B. Kapadia: 109, 110 Josiah Wedgwood & Sons Ltd.: 112 Royal Doulton Ltd.: 114 Edison Electric Institute, New York: 119, 120 Royal Doulton Ltd.: 121, 124 (Top) Royal Doulton Ltd.; photos B. Kapadia (Bottom) General Electric Co., Schenectady, New York: 125 Royal Doulton Ltd.; photo B. Kapadia: 127 Royal Doulton Ltd.: 128, 129 Royal Doulton Ltd.; photos B. Kapadia: 131 Smiths Industries Ltd., Motor Accessory Division, London: 134 Plessey Components Group, The Plessey Company Limited:

188

136 British Iron and Steel Federation: 138, 141 The Morgan Crucible Company Limited, London: 145 Photo Thermal Syndicate Limited: 146 The Morgan Crucible Company Limited, London: 149 Glass Manufacturers' Federation, London: 152 The Morgan Crucible Company Limited, London: 153 Union Carbide Inter-America, Inc.: 156 (Top) Colour photomicrographs Dr. G. T. Boalch (Bottom) Skamol A/S Skarrehage Molervaerk, Denmark: 158 Metco Limited: 159 The Derbyshire Silica Firebrick Co. Ltd.: 160 Hawker Siddeley: 162 Smiths Industries Ltd., Motor Accessory Division, London: 164 Aerox Limited: 165 English Electric Valve Company Limited: 167 Electric & Musical Industries Limited: 168 Consolidated Beryllium Ltd.: 169 *Science Journal:* 175 Royal Doulton Ltd.: 176 (Top) I.B.M. (U.K.) Ltd., London (Bottom) H.M. Postmaster General: 179, 181 United Kingdom Atomic Energy Authority: 183 Brookhaven National Laboratory, New York: 184 United Kingdom Atomic Energy Authority.

The author and publishers wish to thank Mr. Alan W. Norris of Doulton Research Limited, Chertsey, England, for his co-operation in the preparation of text and the provision of illustrations for this book.

Index

Note: Numbers in italics refer to illustrations and captions to illustrations.